Eel Capture Culture Processing and Marketing

Eel Capture Culture Processing and Marketing

David M Forrest

Fig 12 Scientific instruments positioned at
the edge of the eel pond continuously
record pond environmental changes.
Photo L Finley

Fishing News (Books) Ltd
1 Long Garden Walk, Farnham,
Surrey, England

ISBN 0 85238 070 4

Printed in Gt. Britain by
Page Bros (Norwich) Ltd, Norwich

Contents

	Page
List of illustrations	11
List of figures	13
List of tables	15
Publisher's note	17
Introduction	19

SECTION 1—ELVER CAPTURE, HOLDING AND MARKETING

An outline of the life cycle of the eel	21
World wide distribution of eels commercially exploited	24
European eel	24
Japanese eel	26
American eel	27
New Zealand eel	27
Some elver migration patterns	28
Two runs	28
Elver cycles	29
Size variation	29
Factors influencing elver migrations	30
Water temperature	30
Light	30
Tide	30
Freshwater	31
Wind	31
Elver catching methods	31
England	31
Northern Ireland	33
Eire	33
France	34
Japan and Taiwan	34
New Zealand	34
Elver holding	35

	Page
Elver transportation	37
Road	38
Air	38
Elver marketing	39
Far East	39
Europe	41

SECTION 2–EEL CULTURE

Extensive culture	45
Italy	45
Northern Ireland	45
Hungary	46
France	46
Intensive culture	46
Japan	46
Taiwan	46
Australasia	47
Germany	47
France	47
Culture methods	48
Still-water method	48
Flowing-water method	49
Net preserve method	49
Tunnel method	50
Circulating filter method	51
Cultured eel diseases	51
Cotton cap or water mould	52
Bronchial kidney	53
Gill erosion	53
Fin rot	54
White spot	54
Plistophora	55
Anchor worm	55
Bubble disease	55
Nematodes	56
European eel diseases	56
Red disease	56
Cauliflower disease	57

Eel feeds 57
  Silkworm pupae 57
  Raw fish 58
  Compound feed 60
Elver feed 64
Environment 68
  Water temperature 68
  Phytoplankton 69
  pH 72
  Oxygen 72
  Pond waste 74
  Pond water 74
  Sulphur 74
  Nitrogen, phosphate and potassium 74
Pond design and equipment 75
  Pond area 75
  Elver tanks and ponds 77
    Elver tanks 77
    Elver ponds 78
  Fingerling ponds 79
  Fattening ponds 79
Supplementary equipment 85
  Feeding 85
  Handling 97
  Pond management equipment 98
  Security 98
Experimental culture ponds 99
  Aquaria 100
  Elver tanks 102
  Fingerling ponds 102
  Fattening ponds 102
Production and management of eels 102
  Stocking density 102
  Growth rates 105
  Yield 106
  Day to day pond management 108
  Harvesting and selection of eels 108
  Pre-shipment starvation 109

	Page
Shipment	110
A decision whether or not to culture eels	110
Introduction	110
Some criteria and questions	111
Capital requirements and returns	116
Fixed costs	116
Variable costs	117
Revenue	119
The potential for eel culture in Europe	120

SECTION 3–EEL CAPTURE

Introduction	123
Eel behaviour patterns	123
Brown eels	123
Silver eels	123
Methods used to catch brown eels	128
Clotting	128
Spears	129
Eel combs	130
Long lines	130
Baited eel box	131
Baited traps	132
Electrofishing	135
Seine nets	137
Fyke nets	138
Methods used to catch silver eels	139
River weirs or barriers	140
Yana	141
Stow nets	141
Weir nets	142
Fyke nets	143
Fixed fishing installations	143
Eel holding and transportation	144
Holding eels	144
Eel transportation	147
Road	147
Sea	149
Air	150

SECTION 4–EEL PROCESSING

Introduction 153
Killing 153
Cleaning 155
Gutting 155
Freezing 156
Glazing 157
Cold storage 157
Brining 158
Smoking 159
Jellied eels 165
Canned eels 168
Kabayaki 168
Eel dishes 169

SECTION 5–EEL MARKETING

Introduction 173
Weight of wild eels caught annually 174
A. European eel 174
B. Japanese eel 174
C. American eel 175
D. New Zealand eel 177
Value of wild eels caught annually (US $) 178
A. European eel 178
B. Japanese eel 179
C. American eel 179
D. New Zealand eel 180
Local currency value of wild eels caught 180
A. European eel 181
B. Japanese eel 181
C. American eel 181
D. New Zealand eel 182
Average prices paid per ton to eel catchers 182
Eel exports from principal exporting countries 183
Fresh or chilled eel exports/imports 183
Denmark 183
France 184
Netherlands 184

		Page
Japan		185
Frozen eels		186
Denmark		186
Smoked eels		186
Netherlands		186
Some notes on different European wholesale markets		
Introduction		187
Italy		187
France		187
England		187
Belgium		188
Holland		189
Germany		189
Denmark		190
References		193

List of Illustrations

		Page
1	Fine mesh plastic elver dip-nets.	43
2	Glass fibre elver holding tanks.	43
3	Polystyrene containers for transporting elvers.	43
4	Boxes of elvers being loaded into Boeing aircraft for Japan.	43
5	Sorting elvers in Japan for distribution to growers	44
6	Overhead sprinkler to aerate holding tanks.	44
7	Silkworm pupae fed to eels.	66
8	Boiled mackerel for eels.	66
9	Mackerel skeletons stripped clean by eels	67
10	Modern compound feeds replacing former methods	67
11	Doughy pasty feeds prepared for eels.	67
12	Scientific instruments checking temperatures and water content. (title page)	3
13	Electric motor maintaining splasher to ensure oxygen content.	86
14	Splasher paddle located in pond.	86
15	Splasher paddle in action to oxygenize water	86
16	Switch panel ensuring control of machinery and office link.	86
17	Water drainage canal serving elver tanks.	87
18	Lip on elver tanks prevents escape.	87
19	Compressor pump aerates tanks.	87
20	Aeration also secured by blowing air through bottom pipes.	87
21	Greenhouse structure over ponds with polythene removed.	88
22	Massive greenhouse over large elver pond.	88
23	Elver pond greenhouse.	88

24 Three large elver ponds covered by one greenhouse. 88

25 Elvers are trained to feed in covered area. 89

26 Steam pipes raise water temperature. 89

27 Slope to drainage point facilitates catching. 89

28 Electric pumps help water transfer and circulation. 89

29 Flowing water maintains pond levels. 90

30 Drainage channels on dividing walls between ponds. 90

31 Electric water pump facilitates control. 90

32 Final clearance of water helped by pump. 90

33 Taiwan eel farm built above ground. 91

34 Small elver rearing tanks. 91

35 Borehole water raised by pumps. 91

36 Circulation of water through canals and drainage gate. 91

37 Central canal serves fattening ponds. 92

38 Shelter for a feed area easily provided. 92

39 Covered elver tanks in Taiwan. 92

40 Large Taiwan eel farm. 92

41 Prepared food ready for distribution from the mixer. 93

42 Mincing fish and silkworm pupae for feeds. 93

43 Seine nets being dried after use. 93

44 All food ingredients are carefully weighed. 93

45 Bottom mud is carefully removed. 94

46 End of season treatment of ponds. 94

47 Grading rack for sorting eels. 94

48 Moulded concrete blocks are widely used. 94

49 Experimental tanks at Shizouka. 95

50 Detailed layout of experimental tank. 95

51 Drainage canal between tanks. 95

52 Aeration unit and flexible pipe lines. 95

53 Transferring eels from gill-net to collection container. 96

54 Seine net capturing fattened eels. 96

55 Holding fattened eels prior to marketing. 96

		Page
56	Packing live eels for market.	96
57	Small fyke net used in capture of wild eels.	151
58	Fyke net staked out in a lake.	151
59	Eel longshore boat ready for hook and line operation.	151
60	Eel market in Copenhagen.	152
61	Bulk lorry equipped with holding tanks operating in Holland.	152
62	Wooden eel boxes and trays being dried.	152
63	Eels being held in nets before marketing.	171
64	Holding boxes used in Holland.	171
65	Freshly prepared smoked eels.	171
66	Smoked eels being wrapped up for the customer.	171

(Unattributed photographs by author)

List of Figures

1	Distribution of European elvers	25
2	Distribution of Japanese elvers	26
3	Distribution of New Zealand elvers	28
4	Position of elvers in a tidal river	32
5	Layout of a simple elver holding station showing water circulation	36
6	Outline of the main links in the elver marketing chain	42
7	Some changes occuring in the pond environment every 24 hours	72
8	Layout of an elver tank	77
9	Layout of an elver pond	78
10	Layout of a fingerling pond	80
11	Pond wall concrete slabs and their angle of slope	81
12	Construction of a drainage gate	82
13	Structure of an eel 'pool' without and with splasher	83
14	Layout of eel culture farm	84
15	Design of an experimental aquarium	100
16	Design of an experimental elver tank	101

		Page
17	Design of an experimental fattening pond	103
18	Difference in growth rates between male and female European and Japanese eels	106
19	Some stages in processing eels	154
20	Outline of hot smoking kiln design	160
21	Design for simple home made kiln	163
22	Smokery layout	164
23	Stages in the jellied eel processing and marketing chain	167
24	Stages in the production and marketing of eels in Europe	191

List of Tables

		Page
1	Timing of elver seasons and number per kilo	28
2	Weight (kg) of elvers imported by Japan (1971–74)	39
3	Value of elver imports between 1971–1974 into Japan	41
4	Results of net preserve eel culture experiment in sea water	50
5	Results of experiment using tunnel method	50
6	Results of experiment using circulating filter method	51
7	Conversion rate using sardines, head of skipjacks, and pupae of silkworms	57
8	Experimental results using fresh fish feed	58
9	Monthly use of fish feed in Japan	59
10	Conversion rate using compound feed	60
11	The amount of feed fed daily as a percentage of body weight	61
12	The amount of oil added to the feed, as a percentage of the total feed weight	61
13	Feed chemical analysis	62
14	TFRI feed formula	62
15	Eels oxygen consumption per kg/hour	73
16	Area of culture ponds in Taiwan	76
17	Eel pond area in Taiwan and Japan	76
18	Gap through which different size eels will fall	97
19	Pond stocking densities	104
20	Average growth rate of eels in first year	105
21	Turnover of eel culture farm	107
22	Annual production of cultured eels in Japan ('000 tons)	107
23	Eel selection sizes	109
24	Fixed costs per hectare (£)	117
25	Variable costs per hectare per annum (£)	118
26	Annual revenue per hectare (£)	119
27	Processing time for different weight eels	162
28	Summary of weight loss during processing	165

29 Weight of European eels caught (1969–1974)   174
30 Weight of Japanese wild eels caught (1969–1974)   175
31 Weight of American eels caught (1969–1974)   176
32 Weight of New Zealand eels caught (1969–1974)   177
33 Value of European eels caught (1969–1973)   178
34 Value of Japanese wild eels caught (1969–1972)   179
35 Value of American eels caught (1969–1973)   179
36 Value of New Zealand eels caught (1969–1973)   180
37 Average prices paid to catchers per ton of eels (US $)   180
38 Value in local currencies of European eels
    (1969–1973)   181
39 Value of Canadian eels ($) 1969–1973   181
40 Value of New Zealand eels ($) 1969–1973   182
41 Average price paid per ton to eel catchers   182
42 Quantity and value of Danish fresh eel exports
    (1969–1974)   183
43 Quantity and value of French eel exports (1969–1974)   184
44 Quantity and value of Dutch eel exports (1969–1974)   184
45 Quantities ('ooo) imported and exported within
    Europe (1974)   184
46 Japanese imports of eels for 1973 and 1974   185
47 Japan's live eel imports by month from Taiwan 1973   185
    and 1974
48 Quantity and value of Danish frozen eel exports
    (1969–1974)   186
49 Quantity and value of Dutch smoked eel exports
    (1969–1974)   186

Publisher's note

David M Forrest is a Science Graduate of London University, and a post-graduate of Reading University, from which he holds a Diploma in Agricultural Extension Methods. He worked on various agricultural development projects in Africa and India, before becoming increasingly involved in applied market research, and in particular elver capture and marketing.

For the last few years seasonally he had been catching and marketing elvers in Europe and Japan for stocking purposes for inland waters, and intensive eel culture farms. In 1973, he became one of the few people to have the opportunity to carry out an intensive study of eel capture, processing, and marketing in Europe; and eel culture in various stages of development in Japan, Taiwan and Australia. Both these studies were made possible through generous aid given by The Fisheries Development Corporation of South Africa Ltd. Forrest is involved in a stock assessment programme in the Republic of South Africa, as well as in elver marketing in Europe.

This work embodies the salient points of that practical experience and deep research of the literature on all aspects of the eel industry; as such it provides a valuable base for operators and processors.

Introduction

The eel is a fascinating subject. Many people still regard the eel solely as a mysterious undesirable snake-like creature lurking on the bottom of rivers; and do not realise that the national and international eel market is annually worth considerably more than £75m. This trade breaks down into five distinct areas, namely, for elvers (baby eels); fingerling eels; captured wild eels; cultured eels, and fresh and processed eels. Europe and the Far East annually produce 20,000–25,000 tons of eels each. The latter is the main area for eel culture; and the former for wild eel capture.

The economic importance of eels to a number of countries in the world is undisputed, and more and more individuals and organisations are showing an interest in different aspects of this market. However, in spite of the size and value of the eel market, and the growing importance of wild eel capture, and eel culture, so far little comprehensive information has been published. Previous books have tended to describe only one or two aspects relating to eels, without bringing them all together under one cover. This is what this book does do; and I hope it will be of interest to a wide range of readers. Elver capture and marketing; eel culture; eel capture; eel processing; and eel marketing are described in five separate sections.

I write from the viewpoint of a layman, who became fascinated by eels, and asked questions. Perhaps they, too, are the kinds of questions the reader has asked himself, but not found the answers? The topics included in each section are described in practical everyday language without going into baffling detail on the finer points about such subjects as eel diseases. This field belongs to the real experts, and I do not intend to encroach on their territory; but to lead the reader to where the information can be found.

In this book I have brought together all the relevant information published on eels, and where pertinent have added details relating to my own practical experience. I would like to express my sincere thanks to the various authors included in the reference list, for the information I have gained from their material, and to acknowledge the very considerable assistance given to me by the Board of Directors and General Manager of The Fisheries Development Corporation of South Africa Ltd; The Fisheries Resources Division of the Food and Agriculture Organisation of the United Nations; and the many other individuals and organisations I visited in Europe, the Far East and Australasia in 1973.

David M Forrest

Section 1–Elver Capture, Holding and Marketing

AN OUTLINE OF THE LIFE CYCLE OF THE EEL

To begin at the beginning. The hypothetical breeding ground of the European eel, as most people know, is in the Sargasso Sea, some 300 miles north-east of Bermuda in the Atlantic Ocean. Even to this day the breeding of the eel is still a mystery, as no mature male or female has yet been found in this area. Schmidt is accredited as being the first person to define where the spawning ground is. This he did in 1922.

Later in 1967, Bertelsen defined the spawning area more precisely following the 'Dana' expedition of 1966. Numerous small larvae were found in April that year in the south-western part of the area described by Schmidt and only there. No larvae were found during the preceding February cruise and Bertelsen concluded that spawning begins at the end of March in this area.

Hydrographical data from the Sargasso Sea indicates a spawning depth of 100 to 200 m. Boëtus and Boëtus (1967) studied captured silver eels and found the maximum temperature at which normal sexual development would take place was 25 to 26°C. A mathematical approach to the data on temperature and maturation period gave an indication of an optimum temperature of 20°C. The exact methods of mating and fertilisation are unknown though presumably fertilisation is external. The ripe spawn and embryonic yolk sac of larvae contain oil globules and each mature female is estimated to produce between 5–10 million ova.

The development and route of larval migration up to an average length of 75 mm may be best described in Schmidt's own words. 'Spawning commences in early spring, lasting to well on into summer. The tiny larvae, 7 to 15 mm float in waterlayers about 200 to 300 m from the surface, in a temperature of about 20°C. The larvae grow rapidly during their first months, and in their first summer reach an average of about 25 mm in length. They now move up into the uppermost waterlayers, the great majority being found at depths between 50 and 25 m or at times even in the surface layer. Then they commence their journey towards the shores of Europe, aided by the eastward movement of the surface water itself. During their first summer, they are to be found in the West Atlantic. By their second summer they have attained an average length of 50 to 55 mm, and the bulk are now in the Central Atlantic. By the third summer, they have arrived off the coastal banks of Europe, and are now full grown, averaging 75 mm in length, but they still retain their characteristic compressed leaf shaped larval form.'

The appearance of the leptocephali is frail (larval form) and it leads a planktonic life. Its distribution is determined by movements of the currents of the sea, of which the Gulf-stream and the North Atlantic current, are the most important. Not everyone, however, agrees with Schmidt that the Atlantic crossing of the leptocephali takes three years. Brongersma in 1967 working on the loggerhead turtle concluded that this species can be carried over the Atlantic by the prevailing current streams in as little as just over a year. In addition, some earlier workers have estimated that debris can float from the American Atlantic waters to Europe in 13 to 17 months. What is beyond doubt is that the European eel undergoes a long marine larval phase before reaching coastal waters and migrating inland towards freshwater.

Leptocephali are not actively migrating animals and do not use their own strength to execute clearly directed movements. Instead helped by their ideal leaf like form, migration routes and speed are determined by the prevailing ocean currents. There is a definite break in migration when the larvae are fully grown, and for the first time they exert their own activity by staying in the vicinity and west of the 1000 m deep Continental ridge around Europe. Here they manage to stay and metamorphose into elvers over a period covering several months in the autumn. It is not known how the leptocephali recognise the Continental shelf, though it could be due to their ability to pick up vibrations from the ocean floor.

After having become elvers the migration is continued. During the metamorphosis of larvae turning to elvers no feeding takes place. Consequently, they diminish in breadth and length. Nothing conclusive is known about the start of an elver migration at sea, though obviously migration ends when the elvers strike land. The assumption is that elvers, like the leptocephali, use the sea currents and tidal streams to carry them towards the coastline rather than actively swimming and using their own strength.

The elvers experience a second delay in their migration when they arrive in an estuary or an area which can be considered as like an estuary. Here the second metamorphosis or transition takes place. After reaching the estuarine area, elvers gradually develop tendencies to swim near the water surface and to form schools, preferably moving along the bank. Newly arrived elvers do not have the slightest inclination to migrate against a flow of freshwater and even try to swim actively out of it, if they get in it by accident, though they gradually develop a preference for freshwater. Elvers suspend their migration for some time in the estuarine areas and resume it after a physiological change has taken place, which results in an adaptation to freshwater life. Elvers, like leptocephali, cease to feed during this second phase of metamorphosis.

There are a number of different factors which influence the migration of elvers from estuarine waters into freshwater and these are discussed later. The juvenile eel having reached the inland freshwater areas spends a number of years feeding and developing. The total life span depends mainly on the time taken to attain the mature silver eel stage. This is determined partly by sex and growth rate which are strongly influenced by the environment. The age reached by female silver eels is greater than that of males. Frost in 1945 observed in the Windermere district of England an average age of 12 to 13 years with a maximum of 19 years for female eels, whereas the average age of male silver eels was 9 years, with a maximum of 12. The absolute maximum age recorded is that of an eel kept alive in an aquarium in Sweden which reached 85 years.

The feeding and developing phase is followed by a third metamorphosis into a mature eel with enlarged gonads. Mature males are considerably smaller than mature females. A change in colour occurs with the yellowish brown feeding eel turning into a silver eel with a metallic bronze or black dorsal surface. Fully mature silver eels stop feeding after having built up large body reserves of fat to sustain them with energy during their long return trip to the spawning grounds against the flow of the ocean currents. The timing of the migration of silver eels is influenced by a number of factors of which the best understood are, the phase of the moon, the time of year and level of water flow.

Marking experiments provide information about the rate of

migration of silver eels at sea. Lupmann and Mann in 1958 mentioned a minimal speed of 13 km a day, whereas Trybom and Schneider in 1908 gave a maximum speed of up to 50 km a day, with an average top speed of about 36 km a day. There are strong indications that the migration of silver eels in the sea takes place in the upper waters layers. The return trip to the Sargasso Sea spawning grounds at these rates of travel may take as little as 9–12 months.

Therefore, the life span of the eel including the leptocephali, elver, brown and silver eel stages may vary between 15–20 years, and includes two marine and one freshwater phase.

THE WORLD-WIDE DISTRIBUTION OF EELS COMMERCIALLY EXPLOITED

The life cycle of the eel outlined in the previous section refers to that of the European eel only. There are, however, 18 known species of eel in the world of which, at present, four are commercially important. Some species are thought to spawn in the same area and they all follow the same basic life cycle pattern of: a marine phase – freshwater phase – marine phase.

European eel (**Anguilla anguilla**)

The wide area of natural distribution of the European eel is notable. It is possibly true to say eels can be found in every European coastal river. The fact that millions of elvers and eels annually pass through the narrow straits of Gibraltar into the Mediterranean is remarkable as one would expect this area to be relatively inaccessible, especially to a species of fish dependent for its distribution solely on ocean currents.

The intensity of distribution does, however, vary considerably. In Italy, the main focal point for eels is in the rivers flowing into the Northern Adriatic Sea in and around Venice. There are numerous shallow lagoons in this area the most notable of which is Comacchio, from which eels have been fished for many centuries.

The greatest concentration of eels in Europe is to be found in the rivers flowing into the Bay of Biscay, especially the Loire and Gironde Rivers. Here alone the French caught 220 tons of elvers in 1973 for export to Japan, not to mention those also sold in Europe and other parts of the world. This means that nearly 800 million elvers are captured annually in this single area.

Most elver and eel capture in Eire is controlled by the Electricity Supply Board in Dublin and as yet, though suitable catching techniques have been developed, little commercial exploitation has been permitted other than for the stocking of inland waters. The main known concentration is found in the River Shannon. The eel industry in Northern Ireland is well organised and is under the control of The Lough Neagh Fisherman's Cooperative Society based at Toomebridge on the River Bann.

In England elvers are carried inland on the high spring tides in the River Severn and to a lesser extent on the River Parratt which together produce 50 tons of elvers annually. Eels are known to be found on the west coast of Scotland too, but not in any apparent great concentration. The Dutch have built special elver traps on the Ijsselmeer Dam wall, so as to capture migrating elvers. These elvers are used for stocking inland canals primarily in the waters where eel fishermen make their living.

The coastline of Germany is small and it is strange such a strong tradition for eating eels, specially smoked eels, should have built up in a country where eels occur naturally in relatively small quantities. The Germans, to overcome the shortcomings of nature, import large quantities of elvers annually from France, Holland and England to stock inland waters throughout the length of their country. Many eels are caught in the brackish and fresh waters of Denmark and southern Norway and Sweden. The number of elvers captured annually in Europe is a total well in excess of a billion.

Fig 1   Distribution of European elvers is shown by the hatched areas indicated by arrows

Japanese eel (Anguilla japonica)

The exact position of the spawning area of the Japanese eel is unknown, though it has been established it lies somewhere south of Taiwan. Elvers follow the Kuroshio current and drift into Taiwanese estuarine waters. The prevailing ocean currents do not limit the distribution solely to these two countries. Commerical quantities are caught and cultured in Korea and an as yet unknown quantity are found along the Chinese mainland coastline. The spawning area is clearly closer to the rivers these elvers migrate up as Japanese elvers are younger than European elvers when they reach freshwater.

In Taiwan elvers are captured in the rivers near to the cities of Taipei, Ilan, Kan, Changhua and Pingtung. The main focal point in Japan is centred around Hammatsu in Shizuoka Prefecture about 150 miles west of Tokyo, although some elvers are found north and south of this area. The season in Japan when young elvers

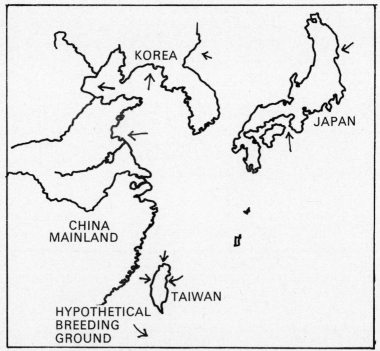

Fig 2 Japanese elvers are widely distributed over mainland river areas as well as in Japanese favoured locations – see arrow pointers

come up the river mouths differs little from region to region. The exact quantity of Japanese elvers captured annually is unknown, though it is probably in the region of 50 tons at the most, about a sixth of the total European catch. This species is apparently subject to far greater fluctuations in supply which maybe in part due to over-exploitation of the wild stock and pollution.

The mottled eel, *Anguilla Marmorata* is found in the same areas as the Japanese eel. It is relatively unexploited because of its unacceptable appearance to consumers. It is probable it shares the same spawning ground area as the Japanese eel.

American eel (**Anguilla rostrata**)

The American eel is thought to spawn in the same area as the European eel, namely, the Sargasso Sea and is distributed all along the east American and Canadian coastline. The Americans do not as yet have a tradition of fishing for eels and elvers and the stocks of many rivers are largely unassessed and unexploited. The adult eel production level in America and Canada is nearly the same.

New Zealand eel (**Anguilla australis**)

The spawning ground of the New Zealand eel is supposed to be south of New Caledonia in the 'Archipelago' Islands. Leptocephali are borne on the East Australian Current to the mainland of Australia. The short-finned New Zealand eel is distributed from west of Melbourne, along the coastline as far up as Brisbane; whereas *Anguilla diffenbachi*, the long-finned eel, which is also found in this region is distributed from east of Melbourne to well above Brisbane. There are no eels west of the State of Victoria.

The distribution of eels in New Zealand is fascinating. Both species are found there though 90% of the elvers captured are *Anguilla australis*. It seems amazing, when considering the relative isolation of New Zealand on the edge of the Pacific Ocean, that elvers can be found in large quantities on both the east and west sides of North and South Island. One can only speculate on the nature of the ocean currents needed to give this distribution pattern. The main concentration of elvers are to be found in the Waikato River, of the west side of the North Island.

Anguilla Australis is referred to as the New Zealand eel here, as it is commercially more important in New Zealand than in Australia though it may be known more familiarly by some as the Australian eel.

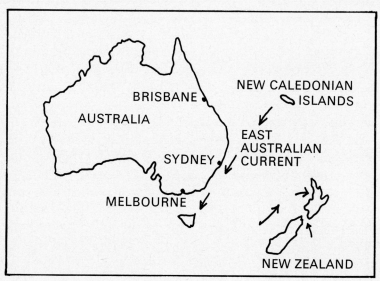

Fig. 3 New Zealand elvers (two species) reach Australian east coast and New Zealand from Pacific breeding grounds

Table 1 – Timing of elver seasons and number per kilo

Species	Season	Number per kilo	Length (cm)
European	December – May	3.600	6–7
Japanese	November – March	6.000	5–6
American	May – August	—	—
New Zealand	August – October	5.000	5–6

SOME ELVER MIGRATION PATTERNS
Two Runs

Marcel Huet in the *Textbook of Fish Culture* records there are two elver or fingerling eel runs each year in Europe. The first involves true-elvers migrating inland from estuarine to freshwater conditions during the winter. These elvers make up the bulk of the elver stocking and restocking trade and are about 7 cm in length, initially transparent, and as thick as a matchstick. Occasionally, larger elvers are caught during this period.

The second run takes place during the summer months of June and July and involves elvers already in a river which are migrating further inland towards new feeding grounds. These elvers, or rather fingerling eels, are 15–20 cm long and the thickness of a pencil. Easily recognisable strings of fingerling eels can be seen at night in good weather swimming several kilometres above the tidal zone. These strings are made up of elvers from the preceding year which have remained in the lower reaches of the river until they have developed and males may make up as much as 80% of this group.

In Germany, fingerling eels are caught in the tidal zone of the River Elbe for stocking inland waters. A similar second season is observed in Australia in November and December and is generally associated with high inland summer rains providing a flow of water to enable fingerlings to continue their migration upstream in large numbers, both by day and night.

Elver Cycles

The quantities of elvers reaching the European coastline show a definite periodicity, not only yearly, but also six yearly, according to Bertin. Every even year is marked by low captures and odd years by high ones. Three years of increase are followed by three years of decrease. Elver catch records from the River Bann and River Severn, however, do not reveal any periodicity at all.

Size Variation

The most obvious features of elver development are the gradual pigmentation and a reduction in length and weight. This reduction is due to not feeding while migrating. The characteristic of early season elvers being larger than those arriving later is well-known. Differences of 6 mm between mean lengths at the beginning and end of a season have been recorded. Elvers are transparent when initially captured, but become pigmented within four to five days, if exposed to daylight.

FACTORS INFLUENCING ELVER MIGRATIONS
Water Temperature
Nothing conclusive is known about what causes the start of an elver migration at sea and the end period when they strike land, but it is strongly influenced by water temperature. In mild winters elvers migrate inland much earlier. It is assumed temperature differences are responsible for initiating migration. The warmer water of an estuary attracts elvers away from the colder sea. However, this opinion is not true in all circumstances.

Most European elvers are first present at a temperature of $4°C$, though they may be seen at temperatures as low as $1°C$. After elvers are on the move they may stop when the temperature becomes too cold. No matter how large the elver run might be, if the wind moves to the north, they immediately disappear and the run stops. Warm water helps bring elvers to the surface otherwise they swim deep in a river thus making them more difficult to catch.

Light
European elvers generally are repelled by light when they first arrive in a river. It is only at the end of their transition period that they are attracted by a strong light. Some fishermen therefore use lights to induce elvers to congregate a small distance under the water surface. Elvers tend to swim in the lower depths of a river on clear moonlit nights.

In practice, European elvers are caught in large numbers only at night. This does not mean a migration will not occur on the high tide during the day but the quantities involved are negligible. Elvers generally bury themselves in the mud or under stones during the day. Interestingly, by comparison, the New Zealand elvers migrate in large numbers during the day. The influence light has appears to vary from species to species and from tidal to non-tidal rivers.

Tide
In Europe and Japan the majority of elvers are caught in the upper water layer as the tide comes in, usually at night. The tide on the River Severn has to reach a certain minimum height before it is considered high enough to bring elvers in on it in sufficient

quantities. Elver migrations on this river coincide with the high spring tides. However, one should not forget a great many elvers migrate annually in the Mediterranean where the tidal influence is practically nil.

Freshwater
Elver penetration of rivers is always made in the direction of a decreasing salinity. Elvers are attracted from the open sea by freshwater brought down by rivers. The stronger the downward flow of freshwater, aided by heavy spring rains, the better the scent elvers get to attract them to continue their inward migration. The force and flow rate of freshwater in a river should be impeded as little as possible by dams, otherwise elvers are not forced to travel along the river banks.

Wind
In Japan the number of elvers coming up a river is large when there is a southern breeze, at a speed of about 2 m per second, and the temperature is warm, between 8–10°C, and there has been a rainfall on the previous day.

ELVER CATCHING METHODS
The fishing equipment used to catch elvers in different parts of the world varies considerably from the traditional hand-made scoop nets to boats fitted with echo-sounders. Generally, the technique employed is specially adapted to suit the particular local environment in which it is to be used and no one method of fishing is appropriate to all catching conditions.

England
The first elver depot in England was founded by a German at Epney next to the River Severn before the 1914–18 war, and tens of millions of elvers were exported to Germany before it was taken over by the Ministry of Agriculture and Fisheries during the Second World War. Today there are two main elver buying companies based there. Many Severn elvers are dispatched to the Continent, particularly to Holland and Germany for restocking rivers and dykes, as the main Dutch and German rivers have their estuaries in the Baltic and North Seas and are thus by-passed by

the great drift of elvers across the Atlantic. Elsewhere in Europe, elvers are much sought after as a delicacy with supposed aphrodisiac properties.

Elvers are caught mainly in distinctive scoop nets, about 1 m long, 60 cm across the top and 60 cm deep, usually made of a strong cheese-cloth or plastic netting stretched tightly over pliant willow and mounted on a long willow handle. The fisherman carefully submerge the scoop with its mouth facing downstream and hold it as close as possible to the side of the river bank. A jutting out point of land is advantageous and this influences the fisherman's choice of position on the bank. The net is held in place for any time up to five minutes, then lifted and the squirming mass of elvers emptied into a bucket securely positioned on the bank. When they are running well, one dip may fill a bucket. As and when a bucket is full, elvers are tipped into shallow holding trays lined with a fine cloth. These are stacked one on top of another, strung together and transported back to the elver depot. Elvers are able to survive for considerable lengths of time out of water but

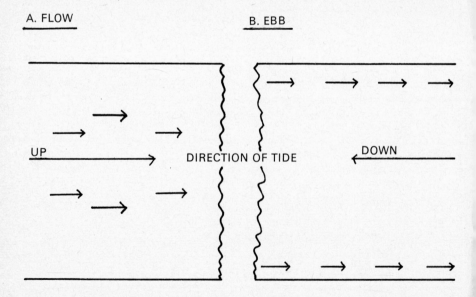

Fig 4 Showing how elvers progress upstream in tidal rivers with the stream flowing up and down

should not be left in a bucket for long lest those on the bottom be suffocated.

Northern Ireland

Special elver ladders have been designed for use on the River Bann at points where the upstream migration is obstructed by a weir or a waterfall. The force of water at the centre of the weir blocks the upstream movement and elvers swim to the side of the river to where the flow rate is slacker. A small hatch regulates the flow of water into a channel built at the side of the weir. A specially woven straw ladder is fitted into this hatch and upstream freshwater allowed to trickle down the ladder into the river below. Elvers are attracted to this water flow and climb the ladder. Their progress, however, is impeded towards the top and they are forced off the ladder into a collecting trap or box placed below the ladder in the channel.

The catching technique has a number of advantages in that it can be placed above the river tidal zone, it ensures every elver is caught and that the trap can be left unmanned and still be completely effective. Catches of 5–6 tons in a season have been recorded on the River Bann, all of which have been released in Lough Neagh for restocking purposes.

Eire

There is no organised system of elver catching in Eire though most rivers are under the control of the Electricity Supply Board. The Board has successfully designed an elver trap which is not dependent on an obstruction in a river for its success. The trap can be positioned at the waters' edge anywhere along the river bank. It consists of a nylon brush which comes to an abrupt end at an inclined groove cut across the timber on which the brushwork is mounted. Water enters the upstream end of the trap through an adjustable slot and runs over a smooth timber surface entering the groove where part flows along the groove and into a pipe and the remainder down through the brushwork. Elvers travelling close to the bank enter the water flowing out through the brushwork and travel up to the groove where they enter a high velocity stream of water and are washed down the side pipe and into a holding tank.

The trap can be set at any point where a 5 cm head of water

can be generated over its length. It is portable and will operate extremely well attached to bridge piers. In good run conditions catches of up to 65 kg per hour have been achieved. It can also be used to catch fingerling eels for restocking inland lakes.

France

The French, the main catchers of elvers, use fine meshed seine or purse nets either trawled from slowly moving motor boats in the river estuaries, or sometimes used from the shore. Some boats are now fitted with echo-sounding equipment which help to locate the area in the river where elvers are massing. Captured elvers are held temporarily on board in a series of tanks, through which water is continually pumped by the boat's engines, before they are transferred to holding tanks on shore. The bulk of the French catch nowadays is exported to Japan though some are still sold within Europe.

Japan and Taiwan

Glass eels or elvers are caught in the Far East by a variety of methods. These may include a small gauze scoop net used by fishermen who wade out into the shallow river water and as they catch elvers, transfer them into a waist pouch before wading ashore once sufficient elvers have been caught. They then transfer them to a bowl covered with a cloth to protect them from exposure to cold air. The elvers are then temporarily placed in water in plastic containers to await buyers. The elvers are extremely delicate and great care is taken not to bruise them. Alternatively, drag nets towed by powered rafts or trap nets are set in places where the river mouths are wide, such as the mouths of Lake Hamanako and the River Tone. Glass eels are caught in estuarine waters all around the coast of Taiwan.

New Zealand

Glass eels accumulate in the lower reaches of a river for sometime before beginning their inland run under high spring tide and new moon conditions. Elvers are captured in fibre glass mesh nets mounted on buoys positioned across the river, which rise and fall with the level of the river. The export of glass eels is now only permitted under certain circumstances and those captured are used for restocking and for intensive culture.

ELVER HOLDING

Irrespective of which part of the world elvers are caught, it is necessary to temporarily keep them alive in special holding tanks, as they are received from fishermen before marketing them or transferring them to culture sites. This allows adequate numbers for a consignment to be accumulated, and those elvers which have been bruised during catching and have died within 48 hours to be removed so that the quality of the sample when it is shipped is not impaired. In addition, temporary holding allows elvers to adjust to a new restricted environment and to begin to overcome the considerable stresses associated with it. Newly caught elvers require very careful management and continual supervision so that the first signs of any possible trouble can be immediately detected. They are generally held at Elver Depots for a minimum of two days and a maximum of five days, although circumstances may dictate otherwise. If elvers are shipped too soon after capture, mortality rates are greatly increased.

Two vital requirements have to be met if elvers are to be kept alive successfully, a continual flow of suitable freshwater and air must be maintained all the time. Large quantities of elvers confined to a small area consume vast quantities of oxygen which must be continually replaced. Fig 5 outlines the layout of a very simple but effective design for an elver holding depot. (overpage)

A roof built over the tanks reduces the amount of stress elvers are subjected to from daylight and provides a covered area under which packaging can take place without any interference from the elements. The ideal temporary holding tanks should be movable, enabling them to be turned over and cleaned thoroughly between tides. Permanent brick structures are not so easy to clean and do provide the elvers with a rough surface which they can adhere to and climb up so as to escape. Fibreglass tanks measuring 2 m × 2 m × 60 cm will hold up to 100–125 kg of elvers each, providing sufficient water and air are available.

Newly caught elvers should be placed in a receiving tank before being transferred to other available tanks. Inevitably as the tide rises, flotsam is carried upstream and can accumulate in the scoop nets. A reception tank allows this to settle and other species of fish to be removed so that the main holding tanks remain clean. Elvers en masse generate a large amount of foam, known as

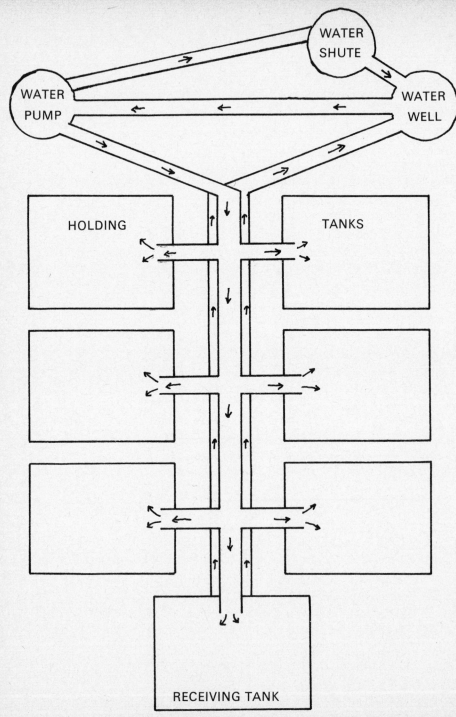

Fig 5 Layout of an elver holding station showing system of water circulation

'vump', which must be quickly removed from the water surface to avoid suffocation. Once elvers have been transferred to clean tanks they should be disturbed as little as possible and different batches should not be mixed.

The daily or hourly management routine should include the twice daily removal of all dead elvers, known as 'whites'. Whites tend to congregate in one particular area of a tank and form their own mortuary. This makes their removal relatively easy without all the live elvers in the tank having to be disturbed. Deaths may be due to either bruising and or bad handling during capture, or to insufficient aeration of the holding tank water. Even under careful management conditions whites may account for up to 5% or more of all elvers caught. A complete loss may occur if, on cold nights, elvers are kept in trays or buckets for too long before being transferred to holding tanks.

In the 2–5 days elvers are held a total weight loss of up to 10–15% can occur due to whites and other factors. Elvers at this stage are still contracting in length and breadth and this will account for a certain amount of weight loss, as well as that caused by stress. No attempts are made to feed elvers before they are shipped.

Much the same routine of managing elvers is followed when they first arrive in Tokyo, Japan or other parts. The main objective of the Japanese at this juncture is to authenticate the survival rate, and it may take up to 24 hours before a liveweight can be agreed. A consignment is then sub-divided and placed in a number of gauze baskets, each containing the allocation of a particular farmer or group of eel farmers. The baskets are suspended in highly aerated tanks through which a continual flow of water is maintained until collection is effected.

ELVER TRANSPORTATION

Elver transportation can be carried out in a variety of ways. The factor governing which system is used depends, to a large extent, on the distance they are to be transported and the cost involved. Elvers may be successfully transported in or out of water. The gill surface of an eel is extremely small compared to the gill surface of other species of fish. In 1964 Krogh showed that eels respire through their skin which provides for about three-fifths of their total oxygen uptake made possible by a special capillary system.

Road Transportation

Two practicable methods are used for transporting elvers by road. Formerly, they were packed in special three-tier boxes, each tier having three 0.5 kg compartments. Eight of the compartments were packed with elvers and the ninth fitted with a large sponge, soaked in river water to keep them moist during the journey, and a generous quantity of ice was placed on top. This method is still generally used for short duration trips and when weather conditions are cool.

Special aerated tanker lorries are widely used today as they allow large quantities of elvers to be transported at one time. Six tanks are mounted sideways on a lorry, together with two air compressor pumps or oxygen cylinders one of which continually bubbles air into the base of the tanks throughout the duration of the trip. The other is held as a spare in case of emergency. Each tank holds up to 200–250 kg of elvers and before the journey begins, salt is added to the tanks to make the water half saline. Elvers can be successfully kept alive for many hours using this technique.

Air Transportation

Elvers are air-freighted many thousands of miles to reach lucrative markets with little loss of liveweight. They are able to survive at least 36 hours in relatively little water and this fortunately means an exporter avoids paying a high freight bill for shipping water from one side of the world to the other. Elvers are packed in polystyrene trays over which is placed a close fitting ventilated lid. Polystyrene has the advantages that it is both light, while at the same time it insulates elvers from sudden changes in temperature. The trays are very easy to handle and because of their strong flexible nature they can withstand a certain amount of rough handling.

1.0–1.2 kg of elvers are packed in each tray, together with a little water and ice. This allows the elvers to remain moist throughout the duration of their trip. The amount of water used must be carefully watched. Elvers die if too much is used simply because they very quickly absorb all the oxygen in the water while their body contact with the atmosphere is reduced. Alternatively, if too little water is used, elvers dehydrate and die. Elvers out of water depend on the atmosphere to meet their oxygen requirements and this is why trays are lugged and ventilated in some way. Ice, besides eventually providing additional water, reduces the temperature in the trays and checks elver mobility and therefore their respiration rate and oxygen requirements. All that can be seen inside a filled tray is a two to three centimetre deep mass of squirming elvers. Trays of elvers are placed in refrigerated trucks to begin their journey to the airport and then overseas. High survival rates are achieved despite the considerable stresses elvers are subjected to one way or another.

ELVER MARKETING
Far East
The main market for elvers in the Far East is in Japan, though a certain proportion of elvers sent from Europe find their way into Taiwan. Slowly, however, other countries in the Far East such as Malaya are beginning to show an interest in eel culture, even though their natural supplies of elvers are low. Table 2 shows the annual weight of elvers imported by Japan in a recent period.

Table 2 – Weight (kg) of elvers imported by Japan (1971–74)

Country of Origin	Year 1971	1972	1973	1974
Indonesia	—	—	—	20
Republic of Korea	9.701	13.461	76.993	84.385
Formosa (Taiwan)	270.666	114.083	45.159	161.400*
France	23.602	70.649	219.277	44.923
United Kingdom	4.571	8.040	8.565	4.655
Italy	7.291	2.660	2.532	—
New Zealand	—	1.595	1.276	583
China (Mainland)	1.253	1.486	3.075	6.670
Hong Kong	176	159	59	340
Canada	148	—	12	—
USA	37	485	895	232
Phillipines	—	1.048	—	—
Morocco	—	—	532	—
Cuba	—	—	256	—
Ryukyu Islands	—	—	—	—
Singapore	780	—	—	57
TOTAL QUANTITY (kg)	318.225	213.666	358.631	303.265

* *includes fingerling eels.*

These figures clearly show the vast trade in elvers for culture in Japan, and the wide range of countries supplying this market. Several different species of eel are imported. A close examination of the figures will demonstrate how rapidly Europe's share in this market has increased. In 1969 Japan imported just over 60,000 kg of elvers. By 1971, this figure had increased five-fold. The Taiwanese figures for 1971 and 1972 include fingerling eels, which are elvers fattened for a few months before being marketed.

No commodity has experienced a rise in price within the span of a few years as rapid as the glass eel in Taiwan. Before the commercialisation of eel farming, the glass eel had no market and was caught simply as duck feed. Later in about 1966, the price for one kilogram of *Anguilla japonica* glass eels was only 50p. The market price in March 1973 was about £500 a kilogram, an increase of 1,000 fold in seven years. This phenomenal increase in price was due to two reasons – the shortage of supply and the heavy buying and high price paid by the Japanese eel importers.

In Japan the market is subject to wide fluctuations in price, but what is clear is that the Japanese are prepared to pay considerably higher prices for their own home caught species of eel, *Anguilla japonica*, than for any other species they may import. The average price the eel farmers paid for a kilogram of elvers in 1973 was in the region of £350, with apparently a maximum price of nearly £900 being reached (¥650 = £1). The capture of elvers is carefully controlled in Japan and farmers are not allowed to catch their own stocks in the rivers but must buy either through the main Trading Houses or from the Eel Farmers Federation based in Shizouka Prefecture.

In sharp contrast the average price farmers paid for European elvers was in the region of £20 a kilo. The assumed reason why the Japanese pay less for European elvers is that they claim their survival rates are lower, as they cannot tolerate the high water temperatures during the summer making them more susceptible to disease outbreaks. In addition, their fattening rate is slower than the indigenous species. It may well be a number of farmers are heavily subsidised to enable them to be able to pay these high prices for basic stocking material. Such is the price to be paid in times of shortage of supply. Table 3 outlines the prices paid in Yen (¥) for elver imports into Japan by country. The Japanese elver import bill came to nearly £6.4 m in 1973.

There is also a growing trade in the export of fingerling eels to Japan, especially from Taiwan.

Table 3 – Value of elver imports between 1971–1974 into Japan (Y'ooo)

Country	Year 1971	1972	1973	1974
Indonesia	—	—	—	363
Republic of Korea	272.802	522.298	1.641.917	854.691
Formosa (Taiwan)	2.200.999	1.517.211	494.329	894.718
France	178.382	550.341	1.744.217	269.979
United Kingdom	43.390	74.098	78.698	28.386
Italy	50.373	27.869	30.566	—
New Zealand	—	14.529	7.543	2.866
China	37.945	55.257	104.690	175.881
Hong Kong	4.276	5.783	9.731	8.504
Canada	878	—	191	—
USA	355	1.342	17.666	5.552
Phillipines	—	22.812	—	—
Morocco	—	—	2.711	—
Cuba	—	—	7.299	—
Ryuku Islands	36.691	—	—	—
Singapore	—	—	—	1.668
TOTAL VALUE	Y2.826.091	Y2.791.540	Y4.139.558	Y2.242.608

Europe

Facts and figures on elver marketing and prices are not so readily available as those in Japan, mainly because there is considerable trade within countries where no border crossings are involved, so elvers pass from company to company undeclared. The main countries buying in elvers are Holland and Germany, though some are also taken by Austria, Spain and Hungary. The annual trade in elvers from France and England is in the region of 50–60 tons which are primarily used for stocking rivers, lakes and dykes.

The main marketing stages elvers pass through in Europe and in the Far East are outlined in Fig 6 overpage.

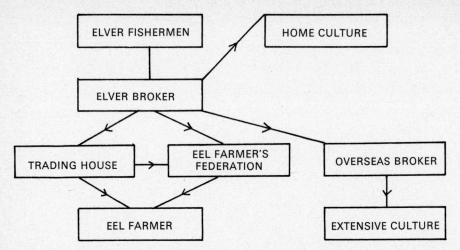

Fig 6   Outline of the main links in the elver-marketing chain

Fig 1 Fine mesh plastic elver dip nets drying in the sun after use at night in the West of England.

Fig 2 Water is continuously circulated in and out of glass-fibre elver holding tanks, when a high stocking density is being kept.

Fig 3 Three kilos of elvers packed and ready for export in light weight, aerated, easy-to-handle polystyrene containers.

Fig 4 Packs of elvers being loaded into the hold of a Boeing 707 aircraft bound for Japan. This trip takes 15 hours, in comparison to the $2\frac{1}{2}$ years that the elvers take to reach Europe in the Gulf Stream.

Fig 5 Newly arrived European elvers in Japan are held in small quantities in well aerated baskets to establish the liveweight. *Photo L Finley*

Fig 6 An overhead sprinkler line improves water aeration at a temporary holding elver station outside Tokyo. *Photo L Finley*

Section 2–Eel Culture

EXTENSIVE CULTURE

The extensive culture of eels can be said to be practised in any place where eels are both unintentionally and intentionally stocked and allowed to grow and develop in an environment where there is a minimum of interference from man, and where relatively low stocking rates are observed. This definition includes eels growing wild in rivers. Throughout Europe, inland waters are stocked with elvers either to complement eels growing naturally there or are introduced to inland waters where no migration takes place. These situations are examples of extensive culture of which the dykes, rivers and lakes of Holland and Germany are the best known examples. There are, however, several other countries in Europe where interesting examples of extensive culture are practised.

Italy

The centre of extensive eel culture is at Lake Comacchio, near Venice in Northern Italy. Here annually 32.000 hectares (80,000 acres) of inland waters fenced off to form 'valli' of varying sizes are supplied with brackish water to produce about 1000 tons of eels. The salinity is regulated by a series of gates controlling the flow of sea and freshwater from adjacent streams and rivers. The elvers migrate in from the sea or are caught along the coastal areas and are transferred to the 'valli' at the fingerling stage. Until recently, no artificial feed was used and the growth of the eels was very slow, taking several years to reach a marketable size. This delay made the whole operation less and less profitable with yields going down from 150–200 kg to 50 kg per hectare. So, more recently, artificial feeds have been used to augment natural foods.

Northern Ireland

Elvers are caught in traps on the River Bann, and then introduced into the 38.000 hectares (94,000 acres) of Lough Neagh. The brown eels are caught in the Lough using long lines and silvers as they migrate out of the Lough back into the River Bann. The annual production has been constant for a number of years at 800 tons.

Hungary

Elvers have been imported from Ireland and France to stock Lakes Balata, Valence and Ferto, following experiments carried out in 1961 and 1962. The stocking rate was very low at 400 elvers per hectare and they took six years to mature to silver eels with an average weight of approximately 650 g. Their growth rate was enhanced by a high average water temperature during the summer months of 26°C. The lakes were usually drained in early spring and late autumn and the eels caught in eel racks postioned in the outlet channels.

France

An example of extensive eel culture is in the shallow waters of Ètang du Thau near Marseilles, where the 8.000 hectares (19,000 acres) of inland water produce about 70 tons of eels annually.

INTENSIVE CULTURE

Japan

Eel culture began in Japan as long ago as 1870 and has since then successively developed from primitive culture into intensive culture. The culturing techniques have been extensively improved. Today compound feeds are being used by 2000 farmers producing 20,000 tons of eels annually. The further expansion of eel farming has, however, been limited by the problem of finding suitable sites with sufficient supplies of good quality water. Much of the data included in this section is based on intensive culture in Japan.

Taiwan

The intensive culture of eels in Taiwan has a comparatively short history. Before 1952 there was no eel culture on a commercial scale due to the limited demand for eel and the consequent lack of interest on the part of fish farmers. The main demand for eels at this time was as live bait for shark longlining. In 1952, an eel farm was established at Taoyuan by the Government. Following this the Taiwan Fisheries Research Institute started an experimental eel farm at Lukang in 1956. In 1966, there were only about 60 hectare of eel ponds in Taiwan; in 1967 the area increased to 80 hectare. The industry developed rapidly in 1968 as a result of heavy demand from Japan for elvers and later, for table size eels. By 1972 there were 1,058 hectare of eel farms exporting over £10m of eels to Japan. Much of the data included in this section is also based on intensive culture in Taiwan.

Australasia
Encouraged by the availability of large natural resources of elvers and fairly beneficial environmental conditions, a number of organisations in Australasia are showing an increasing interest in culturing eels, rather than simply exporting elvers to Japan. Several pilot schemes are under way using in some cases Japanese technology to develop culture techniques suitable to the Southern Hemisphere. In New Zealand, culture experimental work is centred near Auckland whereas in Australia, plans are being developed to possibly establish an eel culture industry in Victoria and Tasmania. No intensively cultured Australasian eels have yet been marketed.

Germany
In the past few years the Germans have been exploring the possibility of introducing eel farming. An experimental eel farm has been built at Muden on the River Moselle consisting of 5 ponds having a total area of 6000 m^2. For a variety of reasons they are a long way from the practical application of this method on a large scale.

In another part of Germany, Koops has tried intensive eel culture experiments using small ponds 1–7 ares in size, and feeding the eels with finely chopped fresh fish and specially prepared pelleted food distributed at the pond water inlet. It was found necessary to stock young eels densely at 150 kg per are. Among the difficulties encountered were that eels escaped and they were difficult to harvest when draining the ponds as they buried in the mud and could be only partly extracted by using electric fishing devices.

The Max-Planck Institute in Ahrensburg, near Hamburg has been carrying out experiments on rearing eels in a warm-water circulating system. Very rapid growth rates were achieved when the water temperature was kept at 23°C.

France
A private company, Compagne des Salines du Midi et des Salines de L'Est, has established an experimental unit at Sétè, near Montpellier to carry out feasibility studies on the culture of the eel. Other

culture centres are planned along the French Atlantic coastline and by the end of 1974 it is estimated that Spain, France and Italy could have 60 hectares of intensive eel farms between them, producing 500 tonnes of cultured eels.

CULTURE METHODS

Five different techniques used to culture eels are outlined. Some of these are still at a very early experimental stage, only theoretically possible and not as yet practised on a large commercial scale, whereas other methods are extensively practised commercially.

Still-Water Method

The culture of eels in a still-water pond is the oldest and most popular method of culture in Japan and Taiwan. The supply of oxygen is left mainly to the mechanism of phytoplankton which grow and multiply in the water. Most eel ponds are literally green from algae growth with only the top five to ten centimetres of the water visible. Algae depend on sunlight for photosynthesis and, therefore, only produce oxygen during the daytime. The balance of oxygen at night must be carefully controlled if high densities of eels are being stocked. Water is particularly susceptible to oxygen deficiencies on hot summer nights. Eels seen gasping at the water surface means there is a shortage of oxygen which should be rectified immediately by turning on a splasher or paddle machine.

Under the still water technique a certain volume of water is allowed to pass through the ponds, but not too swift a current or otherwise the algae are washed away. It is not easy to culture the right type of algae and it is generally necessary to depend on the algae type which grows locally. Recent improvements in water control techniques have made it possible to culture 2.5 kg of eels per square metre of water which is three times the weight that was possible before the war. The area of individual culture ponds is getting smaller with 30–40 are sizes more popular than the large one hectare sizes. The most important point about the still-water method is water control, which means the provision of the optimum environment for the production of high quality phytoplanktons. High productivity depends on how successfully this control is maintained.

48

Flowing-Water Method

The size of ponds used for the flowing-water culture method varies from 150–300 square metres each, constructed in such a way as to provide the eels with an area to hide in when a large volume of well or sea water is made to flow through. This method can only be used in locations where a large quantity of water is readily available to be pumped up from a bore hole or from the sea. Allowances must be made for water shortages during the summer, so that the maximum stocking rate should not exceed the lowest estimated water flow.

The density of eels per unit area that can be kept in a pond depends on the amount of oxygen that can be replenished by the flowing water, therefore, the greater the flow, the greater the stocking density. If more oxygen is required then more water is let through making it necessary to have some form of easily adjustable water-flow control.

Another limitation of this method is water temperature, since if the temperature of the flowing well-water or sea-water is generally lower than that of still-water, the growth of eels is slower. This makes it desirable to start culture with relatively large fingerling eels of about 30 g each. At Ibusuki, in Kagoshima Prefecture, flowing-water culture ponds utilise the rich supply of the local hot water springs. Here culture can be practised all through the year. A few other farmers are experimenting with the flowing-water method, but at the moment it is not used commercially except in one or two isolated cases in Taiwan, in areas where large quantities of sea-water are available.

Net Preserve Method

This method is similar to the net preserve method used in carp and salmon culture and at the present time in Japan this technique is being developed for use in inland lake areas. There is a possibility of it becoming more popular once technical improvements have been made. The following description is based on an experiment made at the Hamanako Branch of the Shizouka Fishery Experimental Station:

'The experiment was made in a waterway of 1.5 metres depth. A new metal basket net (mesh 18 mm × 7 mm), the size of which was 2 m × 3 m × 2 m was made with a bamboo frame. Another net made with a mesh of 8 mm × 8 mm was placed inside the metal net to facilitate the raising and lowering. The eels were cultured in this net. Frozen mackerel were used as feed. At harvest time it was found 72% of the eels had grown to be about 180 g, and their colour was a whitish blue, just the same as those raised in still-water ponds.

Table 4 – Results of net preserve eel culture experiment in sea water

Period of culture	Amount released	Amount harvested	Increase in weight	Amount of feed given	Rate of increase	Conversion factor*
36 days	23.3 kg	38.6 kg	15.3 kg	112.4 kg	166%	7.35

Average water temperature	Average water specific gravity	Output per M²
25.5°C	21.13	7.7 kg

* Calculated from figures drawn from *Aquaculture in Japan* by A Honma.

Tunnel Method

The tunnel method is a technique of eel culture which is limited to experimental work only and is not practised commercially, though it would be quite suitable for small scale culture. The aim of this method is to create an environment similar to the natural habitat of eels, that is, its preference for dark concealed places and to this end a large earthenware pipe is buried in the ground instead of culturing in an open pond. Two concrete water tanks ($1 \text{ m} \times 1 \text{ m} \times 1 \text{ m}$) are constructed 4.8 m apart in the ground, the bottoms of which are connected with earthern pipes of 23 cm diameter. Water from hot springs is used under the flowing water method.

Table 5 – Results of experiment using tunnel method

Period of culture	Amount released	Amount harvested	Amount of feed fed	Rate of increase(%)*	Conversion factor*	Output
30 days	11.0 kg	15.6 kg	22.4 kg	142	4.87	4.6
30 days	15.6 kg	21.6 kg	26.6 kg	138	4.43	6.0
30 days	15.5 kg	18.3 kg	20.8 kg	118	7.43	2.8
30 days	13.1 kg	17.0 kg	14.1 kg	130	3.62	3.9

* Calculated from figures drawn from *Aquaculture in Japan* by A Honma.

Circulating Filter Method

Two ponds are used in this technique, one as a culture pond, and the other as a filter pond. Dirty water is pumped into the filter pond from the culture pond, cleansed and then returned to the culture pond. The cleansing in the filter pond is carried out by the cleansing power of useful bacilli (saphrogenous and oxidising bacilli). In this method it is necessary to carefully watch–the size of the filter pond against the number of eels; the size of filter stones; the thickness of the stone layer; the capacity of the circulating pump; the amount of oxygen in the water; the water quality; and the capacity of the cleansing power of the filter pond. Culture can be carried out in any area where there is the possibility of water shortage. A large amount of eels can be produced in a relatively small pond.

Table 6 – Results of experiment using circulating filter method

Area of pond (M^2)	Culture tank depth	Filter tank depth	Culture in summer	Raising in winter	Amount of circulation of water
33	1.2 m	1.6 m	1 ton	6 tons	40 ton/hr

Days for feeding	Amount released	Amount harvested	Amount of compound feed	Weight increase
38	400 kg	693 kg	413.6 kg	293 kg

The conversion factor was 1.41 and the mortality rate was 10%.

CULTURED EEL DISEASES

To date there are nine important diseases which must be taken into consideration when discussing diseases of cultured eels. In addition, there are a number of other diseases some of which are very difficult to diagnose. The damage caused by disease outbreaks can sometimes be as great as the waste of several hundred of tons of eels worth many thousands of pounds. The increasing use of compound feed makes it possible to give antibiotic medicine to eels through their feed which makes prevention fairly easy for some diseases. There is a marked difference in susceptibility to disease between the Japanese and European cultured eels in Japan and Taiwan. The following notes will aid an eel farmer to identify and understand the more commonly occuring eel diseases. If in doubt, a farmer should immediately contact his feed company or a Government agency, which have a much wider range of facilities and experts available to assist in identification, prevention and cure.

1. Cotton Cap or Water Mould

Cotton cap is the most common and serious disease in eel culture attacking both adult and fingerling eels. It can be easily identified by the growth of thin fungal threads of more or less dirty white or grey on the skin of the head, the mouth, the tail, or the gill filaments. This growth resembles tufts of cotton wool and the disease causes death within one or two weeks.

It was originally thought the sole cause of this disease was a parasitic aquatic fungi, *Saprolegnia parasitica*. However, it is now believed this fungus is only a secondary element which works in succession to, or in combination with, the pathogenic bacterium causing fin rot disease. Eels do not die from the growth of cotton cap on them alone. It is thought the toxic nature of fin rot bacteria works first with its effect multiplied later by the growth of cotton cap.

Attacks usually occur in spring, several days after the first feeding. The damage seems to be greatest when the climate in the spring or autumn is changeable. It tends to happen when additional eels have been stocked in late autumn and the pH of the pond is below 6.0, or above 10.0. The disease can be carried over in ponds from one year to another.

Prevention, as with any disease, is the best form of cure. Feeding should be discouraged by decreasing the amount or stopped entirely when the climate is unstable, and especially when there is a cold spell or sudden change in temperature. The pH of the pond water must always be carefully watched and as soon as the pH shows an abnormal value, adequate measures must be taken. If water is added to normalise the water pH, care must be taken not to lower the temperature of the water too suddenly. The release of additional eels in late autumn should be avoided when the climate tends to become colder day by day. Another form of prevention is to sprinkle lime over the pond bottom to disinfect it when the water is changed.

Cure can be effected by bathing the eels in 0.2 ppm solution of Malachite green or methylene blue to sterilise the fungus, together with treating for fin rot. Alternatively, thiazine and furazolidone should be mixed in the feed for about a month after feeding has started.

2. Bronchial Kidney

Bronchial kidney caused over £1m damage in 1969 when it attacked the main eel culture area of Japan. In 1972, by contrast, it occurred in only a few ponds so the disease may now be disappearing. The disease attacks both the gills and kidneys. The cells on the skin of the gill lamella grow abnormally, increase in size to swell to form club-like structures which stick together.

The kidney, although appearing normal to the eye, shows spots of bleeding all over the medulla and cortex when examined under the microscope. Granular particles form in the renal tube cells, causing the cells and the tube to disintegrate in time and hence, internal bleeding.

The direct cause of this disease is not known though it may be a virus. The effect, however, is a sort of dehydration, the density of the blood becomes high and the amount of body salt drops. Under normal conditions the eels' gills absorb salt from the water in the pond and store it in the kidneys. If the kidneys are damaged no storage takes place and salt is discharged. The body salt content becomes very low and if it reaches a third of its normal level the eel dies.

In the summer, while the eel is feeding, adequate salt is found in the feed. However, in the winter, when the eel is not feeding, there is a chance that the kidneys will be discharging salt while none is being taken in. Bronchial kidney disease is, therefore, also known as winter disease.

There is no effective cure for this disease though the release of disease ridden eels into pond water with a salt concentration of 0.8–0.9% has a remarkable effect in that it lengthens their lives. Treatment can be very expensive as much salt is needed. Bronchial kidney does not attack the European eel, only the Japanese eel.

3. Gill Erosion

Gill erosion is caused by a pathogenic bacterium, *Chondrococcus columnalis*. Infected eels slow down their rate of movement and hang onto the sides of a pond. Nothing unusual can be observed from the outside but internally the gill is damaged, and there is usually a case of anaemia. Even though water quality and the feeding of infected eels are both good, daily deaths may still be considerable.

Slime bacteria attach themselves to the gills and cause their gradual disintegration. The gill tissue may be reduced to a quarter of its original size and the eel experiences considerable breathing difficulties and dies. This disease is not found in the European eel in the Far East.

Gill erosion is very common during the summer months and in October. It can be prevented by adding fresh water to the pond with care not to lower the temperature too suddenly. Damage can be kept to a minimum as long as the discovery is made early and proper measures are taken immediately. Infected eels can be bathed in a nitroflame compound, furazolidone, which is added via the splashers to the pond water at the rate of 0.3–0.4 ppm. Alternatively, sulpha drugs can be administered orally in the feed.

4. Fin Rot

Eels infected with fin rot lose their appetite and start to swim around crazily, before finally coming up and swimming on the water surface. Externally infected eels show severe haemorrhage of the anal and pectoral fins, and a redness and expansion of the anus. Internally, there is hyperemia of the intestine and stomach which are eventually eroded away. Congestion of the liver also occurs. In advanced cases the lower jaw haemorrhages and ulcers form.

Two pathogenic bacterium, *Aeromonas liquefaciens*, and *Palacolobacterum anguillimortiferum* cause the disease. The latter primarily occurs in salt water and the former in fresh water culture. The disease breaks out in the summer months mostly in a water temperature of 28°C.

One form of treatment is to remove infected eels or to add clean fresh water to lower the pond water temperature. Thiazine can be orally administered at the rate of 20 mg per day for each 100 g weight of eel and treatment continued for about a week. Again, eels can be bathed in furam or sulpha drugs. Cotton cap frequently occurs as a secondary infection with fin rot.

5. White Spot

White spot is a well-known fish parasite. Externally a number of grey or white spots appear on the fins and skin of eels each about 0.5–1 mm in diameter. The periphery of the spots begin to bleed when the condition becomes more serious. The disease is caused by a parasitic protozoa and ciliates such as *Ichthyophthirius multifillis* which penetrate the mucous coat and the upper layer of the epidermis.

It attacks elvers or eels less than 10 cm in size, and occurs mostly in May and early June. By itself white spot does not cause much damage but it is often accompanied by other diseases which do. Infected eels should be bathed several times in methylene blue or copper sulphate. The Japanese eel was formerly resistant to white spot though since the introduction of the European eel it has suffered from attacks. The external parasite cannot tolerate saline conditions, so the addition of salt to the pond water is another form of treatment.

6. Plistophora

Plistophora anguillarum is a parasitic microsporidium which attacks the eels' muscular system penetrating deep under the skin into the muscles, thus making cysts. The eel gradually gets thinner and thinner, growth stops, and the body surface becomes uneven and hollowed.

There is no effective treatment as the parasite's spore has a heavy outer shell which chemicals are unable to penetrate. Infected eels should be removed. Smaller eels (1–20 g) and Japanese eels are more frequently infected than European eels.

7. Anchor Worm

The anchor worm, *Lernaea cyprinacea* is an ectoparasite, living mainly in the eel's mouth and causes haemorrhage spots on the lower jaw. In advanced stages it even prevents the eel from shutting its mouth and makes it unable to take in feeds. The best method is to prevent rather than cure, and this is done by sprinkling the water with 4 ppm diptrex in the spring or by using masoten at the rate of 1 g/400 litre.

8. Bubble Disease

Bubble disease occurs early in the season and mainly attacks elvers, forming a bubble-like tumour on their head. Elvers refuse to feed and begin to waiver in their swimming. The disease occurs when the water is over saturated with oxygen and nitrogen gas. This condition can be removed quite quickly by adding fresh water of a low temperature.

9. Nematodes

Anguillicola grobiceps, is a nematode which affects the eel's air bladder. More than 20 can accumulate there growing into a maximum length of 3 cm each and they cause severe haemorrhage, in particular, in June and July. 10–15% of eels in their natural environment are affected by this nematode. *Grobiceps* has no detrimental effect on the Japanese eel which continues to grow almost normally even though affected.

The European eel is weak against this disease and as many as 35–50% can be infected. There is no effective treatment yet, though when the young nematodes are released from the air bladder into the pond, they are susceptible to formalin.

There are a number of other internal and external parasites and bacterial diseases which are found in cultured eels, though none of them are as important as those outlined above. In salt-water plankton are less stable and the oxygen can decrease to a low level. In spite of the attractions of salt water, from a reduction in disease occurrence point of view, only perhaps one per cent of culture ponds in Japan are salt water types.

EUROPEAN EEL DISEASES

The diseases outlined in the previous section were those commonly occurring in Japanese and European eels under intensive culture conditions in Japan and Taiwan. In Europe, intensive culture is practised only on a limited experimental level. There are, however, one or two commercially important diseases which have been identified in eels in their natural environment.

Red Disease

Red eel disease, similar to that causing fin rot in the Far East, can attack eels in both fresh and salt water. In salt water the disease is caused by *Vibrio anguillarum*. It thrives in water with a salinity of about 1.5 to 3.5 per cent NaCl and is found in the German Bight, Baltic and the Mediterranean. In freshwater the disease is caused by a bacteria *Pseudomonas punctata* which, in contrast, thrives in a salinity of less than 0.8 per cent NaCl. Dutch and English eel merchants are well aware of this disease and regularly change the eels they are holding from freshwater to saltwater and back again as a precaution against red disease.

Cauliflower Disease
Diseased eels bear tumours mostly on the snout and also on other parts of the body which prevent them from burying in the mud and from foraging. A gradual deterioration in condition occurs and infected eels become unsaleable because of their repelling appearance.

The cause of the disease is unknown, though it is thought to develop in brackish water and is carried into freshwater by infected eels. Between the years 1957–1959, 5–6 per cent of the eels of the Lower Elbe were infected. In 1967, 12% were diseased.

EEL FEEDS
There is little difficulty in inducing eels to feed in captivity and, unlike most other fish, they will thrive on practically any diet which is mainly of animal protein food. Over the last 50 years the types of feed used by Japanese eel farmers has developed through three distinct phases–silkworm pupae, raw fish, and compound feed–although there is still a considerable overlap between these phases.

Silkworm Pupae
Silkworm pupae were originally in plentiful supply when eel culture was carried out only on a limited scale. Pupae were ground down and fed to eels. There was, however, soon insufficient pupae to supply the demands of large scale production and a further disadvantage was that pupae became unavailable during the winter months. Pupae also formed the main feed of eels during the initial development stage of eel farming in Taiwan, but with the

Table 7 – Conversion rate using sardines, heads of skipjacks and pupae of silkworms

| STOCKING | | YIELD | | AMOUNT OF FOOD |
Pond area (m^2)	Weight (kg)	Total (kg)	Total (kg)	Conversion rate*
3.465	2.380	5.870	37.300	10.69
7.000	3.560	9.520	45.200	7.58
6.380	3.510	10.000	70.500	10.85
6.510	3.310	11.300	62.000	7.76
4.720	3.350	12.400	92.800	10.25

* Calculated from figures drawn from *Aquaculture in Japan* by A Honma.

decline of the silk industry supply of pupae became inadequate and farmers switched to using trash fish and scraps from the fish processing plants.

Eels were stocked at the rate of 0.5 to 0.7 kilograms per square metre, and in a feeding period lasting between 180 and 230 days yielded between 1.3 and 2.6 kg per square metre of water. A vast volume of feed was used amounting to 307 tons in the five ponds included in the survey giving the figures. This was fed on average at the rate of 19.6 kg per square metre per year to produce 32.980 kg of eel flesh. It is easy to appreciate the difficulties involved in finding adequate supplies to meet this demand and it is made worse by a low conversion rate of over 10 kg of feed to 1 kg of liveweight gain.

Raw Fish

Raw fish such as mackerel, atka fish, saury pike, miscellaneous types of ground fishes, tuna, bonito heads, and fish offals are widely used in Japan and Taiwan, when available at a reasonable price.

These fish can be fed either whole or minced up. Fresh or frozen whole fish are strung on a long wire or string through their eyes or gills, then dipped into boiling water for a few minutes to soften their skin otherwise eels cannot bite into them, before suspending them in the water at a fixed feeding spot. Alternatively, trash fish or scraps are minced in a grinder and mincing machine to form a thick paste, which is then placed in a wire basket and lowered to a point just below the surface of the eel pond. On a few eel farms, the trash fish may be cooked before mincing; the advantage being that less bone is included in the final paste as the meat separates from the bones while cooking.

Table 8 – Experimental results using fresh fish feed

STOCKING Weight of eels (kg)	YIELD (kg)	NO. OF DAYS	AMOUNT OF FOOD Total (kg)	Conversion rate
112.5	265.8	203	435.1	5.43
98.5	242.6	169	334.1	5.80
65.0	102.1	194	282.9	6.63
70.0	258.5	177	281 9	4.82
131.5	267.7	133	319.9	6.99

The above figures are extracted from *Aquaculture in Japan* by A Honma

58

The conversion factor for 30 g fingerling eels cultured with fresh fish feed varies between 4.8 and 6.9, which is a much improved rate in comparison with silkworm pupae.

The quantity of fish feed given per day is between 5% and 15% of the total weight of eels released in a pond, with 8% daily as the

Table 9 – Monthly use of fish feed in Japan

Month	Per cent of total amount fed
March	1
April	5
May	12
June	12
July	13
August	21
September	20
October	12
November	4

normal accepted level. Fresh fish feed is usually much cheaper than compound feeds, when supplies are available. Few eel farmers use artificial feeds exclusively.

These figures indicate no feeding is carried out in December, January and February and a negligible amount in March unless artificial heating of water is used. Eels hibernate for a third of the year. August and September are the peak feeding months and it is during this time that eels should be offered as much food as acceptable.

There are, however, a number of disadvantages in using fish feed. Inevitably it is not possible to remove all the bones from the fish before mincing. These bones are indigestible and as the eel feeds, they fall to the bottom of the pond, and gradually accumulate as undesirable waste matter and become a health hazard unless steps are taken to remove them regularly. There are, also, seasonal variations in the quantity and quality of fish available, so continuity of suitable supplies cannot be guaranteed throughout the year. It is very expensive to cold store fish for out of season use. In addition, fish carry bacteria in their guts and this can possibly infect eels if it is used. Stringing and mincing up fish is also very labour demanding.

Compound Feed

The general trend in eel culture is now to use more and more compound feed instead of fresh fish feed and since 1962 in Japan the use of compound feed has rapidly expanded. In 1965, about 2,300 tons were used, and the next year it had increased to 9,600 tons. By 1969, compound feed made up about 80% of the amount of feed fed to eels with a total consumption in excess of an estimated 36,000 tons. At the present time compound feed accounts for 90–95% of the feed used.

In its application compound feed powder is mixed with water and vitamin oil to produce a paste. For example, 20 kg of compound feed powder is mixed with an equal weight of water to which is added 0.6 kg of oil. The sticky paste is then put in a net or wire cage or a gauze tray and hung at water level for 10 minutes for eels to feed from. Care should be taken not to offer eels more feed than they can eat at any one time.

Every eel pond is provided with a feeding platform from which the feed is lowered. Feeding time is early in the morning. The low night oxygen level has been dissipated by then and the daytime maximum oxygen level is yet to come. The appetites of eels are best when the oxygen level is building up, and not in the evening when it is declining. If an aerator paddle is placed near the feeding point and switched on at feeding time it encourages the eels to feed. The eels in the pond, having learnt where and when they are fed come quickly to the wire basket, enter through the mesh and literally bury themselves in the paste, eating voraciously, making a sucking noise similar to pigs. On muggy days eels will not eat much and

Table 10 – Conversion rate using compound feed

STOCKING Weight of eels (kg)	YIELD (kg)	TEMP. 0°C	AMOUNT OF FOOD Total (kg)	Conversion rate*
1.0	1.7	11–22	2.7	3.86
13.0	24.5	22–24	17.8	1.54
35.0	61.0	23–28	30.6	1.18
75.0	132.7	19–25	83.0	1.44
6.0	8.7	20–22	5.4	2.04
8.2	11.4	19–22	7.4	2.31

* Calculated from figures from *Aquaculture in Japan* by A Honma.

intake varies from day to day. Feed is best presented on a tray which avoids the build up of wastage and enables daily observations to be made as to whether or not the amount of feed offered should be increased or decreased.

The results clearly show the improved conversion rates achieved with compound feeds and how they progress as the water temperature level increases. A temperature of 23–28°C appears to give the optimum conversion results for compound feed.

The amount of compound feed fed daily and the amount of oil added to the feed depends on the prevailing water temperature and the experience of an individual eel farmer. Table 11 should be taken as a guideline only.

Table 11 – The amount of feed fed daily as a percentage of body weight

Feed Type/Water Temp.	18°C	18–23°C	23–28°C	28+°C
Elver	3.5	3.5–5.0	5.0–6.0	3.5–5.0
Fattening Compound	2.0	2.0–2.8	2.8–3.2	2.0–2.8

Elvers at all temperature levels take in more feed proportionately than fattening eels, and up to a critical water temperature level of 28°C the quantity of feed offered should be gradually increased. In order to achieve the maximum rate of growth elvers are offered as much food as they will accept without over-feeding.

Table 12 – The amount of oil added to the feed, as a percentage of the total feed weight

Feed Type/Water Temp.	18°C	18–23°C	23–28°C	28+°C
Elver	0	0–3	3–5	0–3
Fattening Compound	0	5–7	7–10	5–7

Fattening eels can absorb substantiately more oil than elvers. Every eel farmer has his own ideas about how much oil to add and amounts used vary with the stages of eel development. It is desirable an eel should have a high body fat level when marketed so the oil content of a diet can be increased towards the end of a feeding programme.

The type of oil used varies from farm to farm. Generally, a vegetable oil containing vitamins A, D_3 and E is used by itself as it is much cheaper than cod liver oil. It has, however, been proved both experimentally and in practice that a mixture of vegetable and cod liver oil in a ratio of 2 : 1 is the most favourable for growth, whereas cod liver oil by itself, is the least favourable.

The level of mineral mixture is also another important factor for growth. Eels kept on diets containing either a 1% mineral mixture or lacking it, stopped growing after two weeks then lost body weight before dying. The higher the level of mineral mixture the better the growth. The maximum body weight gain was recorded with a mineral content of 8% under experimental conditions. Results clearly indicated eels require more minerals in their diet than salmonids.

Two types of feed are generally used during the fattening programme depending on whether elvers or developing eels are being fed. Naturally, the nutrients included in compound feeds vary

Table 13 – Feed Chemical Analysis

Analysis	Elver Feed	Fattening Feed
Protein	48	46
Fat	4	2
Fibre	1	1
Ash	13	13
Moisture	12	13

Table 14 – TFRI Feed Formula

Constituent	Percentage (%)
White fish meal	61
Gamma starch	14
Defatted soybean powder	10
Fish soluable, dried	5
Yeast powder	10
Vitamins	1
L-Lysine	0.1
D.L. Methionine	0.1
Binder	0.2
Anti-oxidant	0.2

from manufacturer to manufacturer but as a guideline a chemical analysis break-down into the percentages is shown in Table 13.

The optimum level of protein in a purified diet for eel has been shown experimentally to be 45% protein for a maximum rate of growth at 25°C. The Taiwanese Fisheries Research Institute (TFRI) began experiments on the formulation of an artificial feed for eels in 1966. In 1968, they produced a mixed compound feed in powder form with the formula given in Table 14.

The above formulation was compared with minced trash fish feed in a 90–day experiment. The water temperature during this time varied between 9.6 and 18.6°C (very low). The conversion rate of the artificial feed was 2.45, compared with 13.49 for trash fish. As a constituent of a feed, white fish meal is preferable to brown fish meal as it produces a faster growth rate, though the increased price must be justified by improved productivity. Brown fish meal tends to oxidise and becomes harmful to the eels' health. The finer the particle size, the better the feed, as this produces a smooth paste helping to activate the eels' appetite. 0.35 mm mesh size is usually used on a grinder, and potato starch is used in the diet to make it more sticky as the starch swells up.

There are a number of advantages to be gained from using compound feed other than better growth rates. It is much lighter than fresh fish feeds, it is ready mixed and arrives as a powder in a bag so it is easy to handle. It does not need any refrigeration. As the mix is made up into a sticky paste, it does not disintegrate and therefore no extra organic matter falls into the pond. The main advantage of compound feed is the convenience in handling. The feed can be prepared in a few minutes by using a mixer thereby saving a great deal of time and labour. The steady production of high quality feed for eels has helped to reduce the number of labour hours needed for eel production, thereby stimulating increased interest in eel culture as an industry. Before factory produced mixed feed was available it was necessary to secure fresh fish for feed. The labour and time that went into the purchasing, transportation and then the preparing (thawing, crushing, bone removing and boiling) of the fresh fish feed was great. Since eel culture is, in most cases, a family concern, the limitations in labour available for other jobs consequently restricted the size of production units. The steady output of a uniform quality compound feed makes it possible to purchase supplies with no worry about shortages or change in quality.

In 1965 a survey of 167 eel farmers using compound feed was made in Shizouka Prefecture. The survey showed that 56% of the farmers used compound feed only and the daily amount of feed given was 2–3% of the weight of stocked eels. In most cases these farmers were adding about 10% of oil to the compound feed. The remaining farmers were using compound feed together with fresh fish feed, but in some instances the compound feed was used first followed by fresh fish feed, while in other cases they were both used together in various proportions.

Of all the farmers 30% said that eels adapted well to compound feed at the very beginning of feeding. They also agreed the growth rate as well as the quality (pale blue and white colour) of eels cultured with compound feed was good. On the other hand the shortcomings of using compound feed were; eels were rather weak against handling; more days were needed for the pre-shipment starvation process; and the loss of weight during the winter months was 20% or about twice that of eels fed with fresh fish. Enlargement of the liver was observed in eels fed on compounds which is said to be attributable to the carbohydrates in the feed.

There has been a search for a cheaper source of protein as the price of fishmeal is continually rising. One potentially cheap protein source is that derived from yeasts grown as liquid hydrocarbons. There is a report of good results with eels when this protein is substituted for a part of the fishmeal. However, public opinion may be against the future widespread use of artificially produced protein.

ELVER FEED

The previous section dealt almost exclusively with the different components taken into consideration in the preparation and administration of a feed suitable for fingerling and fattening eels. But perhaps the most important initial objective in eel culture is to satisfactorily train elvers to accept feed and then gradually convert them to take specially formulated compound feeds.

Elvers have very small mouths and this limits the size and type of feed they can accept initially. They will only take in very small particles and getting elvers to accept feed is a question of patience, careful training, and close observation on the new stock.

At the start of the feeding programme a number of different types of feed can be offered to elvers and these include small earthworms, shrimps, tubiflex worms and daphnia. These may be offered either on a dish which floats on the water surface or in a basket lowered to the bottom of the pond at night. Some eel farmers treat the tubiflex with 0.2% sulfamonomethoxine solution for one hour and wash them before feeding them to elvers. To begin with elvers are reluctant to eat, however, soon one or two get the idea and others then follow suit. Any unaccepted feed should be removed immediately and none allowed to accumulate in the water otherwise it could become a health hazard.

After a few days a number of elvers will have begun to feed making it possible to gradually substitute some of the diet with either finely minced fish meat free from bone or with a compound feed. Some farmers mix fish meat with formula feed in a 7:3 ratio respectively. This has shown good results in low water temperatures. Compound feed is mixed up into a finer paste than for eels to make it more digestible to the elvers. This same feed can be fed right through the growing period

Since eels are nocturnal in habit and feed mainly during the night, the feeding spot of the pond should be a darkened place sheltered on four sides by boards. The amount of feed taken in by elvers depends on the condition of the water and the weather but it is best to give about 30% of the total weight of elvers released in a pond in several rations, between 8 a.m. and 2 p.m. During this period of time elvers are actually fed ad lib. Elver feed intake is at its highest during their first few months of captivity and greater than during any period of captivity and it follows the fastest rates of growth are recorded at this stage.

All the elvers in any one tank must be uniform in size, otherwise the larger elvers will eat the smaller elvers as cannibalism is common among young eels. In addition, larger elvers tend to barge the smaller elvers out of the way at feeding time further worsening their plight. Experience indicates that elvers can be trained within 21 days to accept the compound feed outlined as whole or part of their diet.

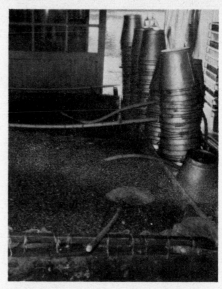

Fig 7 Large numbers of silkworm pupae are kept moist before they are minced and included in an eel's diet.

Fig 8 Lightly boiled mackerel are strung together and fed to eels. The flesh is stripped from the bones in a matter of minutes by ravenous eels.   *Photo L Finley*

Fig 9 Strings of mackerel skeletons are hung in the sun to dry out after being stripped of their flesh.   *Photo L Finley*

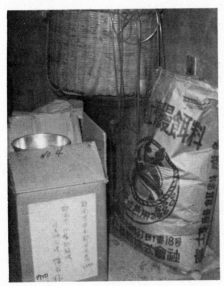

Fig 10 Eel compound feed powder arrives at the farm in paper sacks, just like trout feeds.

Fig 11 A doughy pasty feed compound is offered twice daily to eels in mesh baskets suspended from a covered feeding area.

ENVIRONMENT

The maintenance of a well-controlled environment is vital for the successful culture of any species of fish and the eel is no exception to this rule. A thorough understanding of the many different factors regulating the delicate balance of pond life enables the eel culture farmer to control and manage his fish so that the eel sustains the maximum growth rate throughout its life span. If an eel's growth is retarded in any way due to exposure to an unsuitable environment, a farmer's costs will increase proportionately with a resultant adverse effect on profitability.

Water Temperature

The most important environmental factor regulating the rate of growth, if any one factor can be isolated, is water temperature. It has a profound effect on the mobility and general well-being of eels. Below $12\,°C$ eels are generally inactive. They then rest on or below the mud or stones on the pond base and show very little interest in taking feed, so that their growth is minimal.

Above this temperature, they gradually become more and more active and correspondingly take in an increased amount of feed, and hence reach market size more quickly. The guide to the amount of compound feed fed as a proportion of the eels total bodyweight and the prevailing water temperature clearly show this. At $18\,°C$, it is recommended 3.5% of the bodyweight is offered as opposed to 6.0% at $23\,°C$ to $28\,°C$. The optimum temperature to enable the maximum rate of growth to be achieved lies between $25\,°C$ and $28\,°C$, though there is some variation between species. Japanese eels can tolerate higher temperature levels than European eels which tend to become rather lethargic in high temperatures and generally uncomfortable. In 1969, a large number of European eels died without any signs of disease or parasites when they were exposed to a water temperature of $30\,°C$. Conversely, the European eel continues to feed at a lower temperature level than the Japanese eel. There appears to be a correlation between the optimum culture temperature and the temperature of each species' natural environment. The temperature range for the Japanese eel growth is $12\,°C$ to $28\,°C$, and that for the European eel is $10\,°C$ to $26\,°C$.

In practice an eel farmer, when considering the possible location for a farm, calculates the number of months of the year when the average water temperature will be above 20°C. He can expect this to occur in ponds exposed to the elements for five months between May and September in the Far East. An increasing number of farmers, however, are adopting (according to their financial means) a variety of methods for raising their pond water temperatures during the other months of the year. In the northern hemisphere eels are generally put on the market in September and October, and as a result there is no real point in promoting growth by raising water temperatures at this end of the season. The main area for improvement is at the beginning of the year so as to increase early out of season growth rates and to decrease mortality rates. More specifically, farmers concentrate on elvers rather than eels carried over from the previous season, as at this early stage of development faster rates of growth are shown and heating costs can be spread over a larger population as stocking densities are considerably higher.

Both greenhouses and artificial heating at a high cost are used in Japan whereas in Taiwan, which is closer to the Tropic of Cancer, the natural environmental temperature is always a few degrees warmer, fewer farmers resort to artificial heating. The heating of water starts as soon as the first elvers arrive in November and continues until April. Farmers aim to maintain the heated water temperature at 20°C to 25°C whereas the outside temperature may be as low as 5°C in February. All heating is turned off as soon as the outside temperature reaches 20°C and the young eels are transferred to outdoor ponds. A few fortunate Japanese farmers overcome the need to heat water by locating their farms near to warm water springs. There are also a number of pilot schemes in both Europe and Australasia applying the same principle and carrying out experimental culture using heated power station water. The natural water temperature in Europe can be seen to be the main factor limiting culture in that part of the world at the present time. The section on pond construction deals with the design and layout of heating equipment.

Phytoplankton

A normal healthy eel culture pond is dark green in colour due to the growth of phytoplankton. Under the still-water method of culture phytoplankton carry out a number of important roles in the pond.

They control the oxygen content of the water and the pH level as they photosynthesise during the day. In addition, plankton absorb the eels' excretory products as a source of food on which they depend for their growth and multiplication, though a good farmer takes steps to stop this from becoming too excessive at any one time. It is possible, by maintaining the phytoplankton at a suitable level, to control the rate of sedimentation of organic matter, the decomposition of bacteria in the pond bed soil and the absorption of decomposed products.

There are unfortunately, however, a number of limitations involved in depending on phytoplankton to maintain the pond pH, oxygen level and the rate of breakdown of excretory products, in that their behaviour is somewhat erratic. They grow and develop in cycles and once their number in the pond has reached a certain level they suddenly all die. This immediately has an adverse effect on the various factors they control and until a new cycle has been initiated, the growth rate of eels is badly impaired. In addition, phytoplankton only photosynthesise during the day and even then they are dependent on sunlight. On dull days and at night their performance can also have a hindering effect on the eels' growth rate.

There are a number of reasons why phytoplankton can suddenly die off. The decomposition of organic substances on the pond bed may not be proceeding smoothly and this could result in the phytoplankton not being able to obtain their growth. Alternatively, although there may be plenty of nutritious salts available, there could be a shortage of carbonic acid in the water, which stops their growth and will eventually cause their death. Perhaps the most common cause of phytoplankton deaths is a sudden abnormal multiplication of zoo-plankton in the water which devour the phytoplankton. Well-managed ponds normally have a balanced ratio between phytoplankton and zoo-plankton of 97:3.

The external symptoms marking the death of phytoplankton which a farmer watches for is a sudden change in the colour of the pond water in a very short period of time from a dark green to a dark brown or sometimes a clear colour. This change in colour is more often referred to as 'change in water quality'. Eels can be seen swimming close to the water surface in search of oxygen; and they lose their appetites, which, in severe cases, can result in them dying off in large numbers.

A change in water quality is most likely to occur in the rainy season of May and June and again in September and October, or at any other time in the year when the weather conditions are unstable. There are a number of observable signs in the pond which warn a farmer that a change of water quality is imminent unless he takes preventative action. These signs include, the transparency of the water being more than 10 cm for longer than 10 days, the pH value of the water being above 9.5 in the morning or below 7.0 during the day, and more than 3 ppm of nitrogen in the form of ammonia being detectable in the water.

A change in water quality can be prevented by scattering lime on the pond base at a rate of 60–100 g/m^2 at the end or beginning of the season before the pond is filled with water. This improves the condition of the bed soil and the quality of water near the bottom. In the case of a change beginning to occur, the application of a 0.2–0.3 ppm solution of Diptrex to the water in time can prevent the abnormal multiplication of zooplankton. In severe cases, the pond should be immediately drained and eels transferred to a spare pond. Alternatively if the pond is not to be drained, splasher paddles should be turned on all the time to maintain the oxygen supply until the phytoplankton level is restored.

On the technical side there are many kinds of plankton found in eel ponds all of which have different effects on the chemical balance of the pond according to how they multiply in response to changes in the climate, water temperature and other seasonal changes. Green algae include *Scenedesmus*, *Pediastrum*, and *Chlorella* which appear early in spring and again in the autumn. When *Scenedesmus* is the main component phytoplankton in the ponds then eels have a good appetite, whereas when *Pediastrum* and *Chorella* become the main components the eels' appetite drops. Blue-green algae such as *Nicrocystis* and *Chlorococcus* are the best suited phytoplankton for an eel pond and they appear mainly in the spring and the summer. *Anabaena* and *Oscillatoria*, two other blue-green algae, appear in the autumn and when these occur the appetite of the eels drops. The main zooplankton on the other hand found in ponds are rotifers and water-fleas.

pH

The pond water pH fluctuates according to the amount of oxygen phytoplankton produce from photosynthesis as well as from the rise and fall in the amount of carbonic acid from eels and plankton during respiration. The optimum daytime pH is between 8.0 and 9.0, whereas at night when no photosynthesis takes place, this level will drop to about 7.0. It is unlikely the daily variation in the day and night pH level has a beneficial effect on the eels growth rate. In addition, on rainy or cloudy days, the function of assimilation is weakened thus lowering the pH value. The annual liming of ponds helps maintain the alkalinity of the water.

Ponds located on acid soils usually have a pH between 4.5 and 6.5 and here it can be expected both the growth and feeding activity of eels will be badly checked.

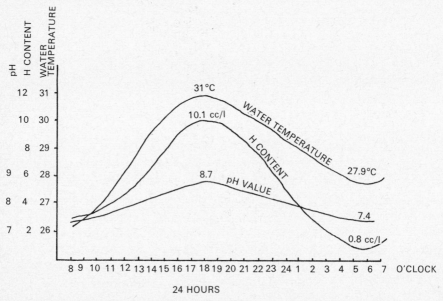

Fig 7   Some changes that occur every 24 hours in pond environment

Oxygen

Oxygen is supplied to the water by phytoplankton as the product of their photosynthesis and from the air. It is consumed mainly by the eels, as well as by phytoplankton, zooplankton, the pond bottom accumulation of dead plankton, remnants of feed and excrements of eel as they decay and decompose. When the weather is sunny and fine the surface water soon reaches saturation point with dissolved oxygen. By contrast the oxygen content at the bottom of the pond may be comparatively low due to the active decomposition of organic matter. At night time photosynthesis ceases and no oxygen is produced by the phytoplankton. Unless remedial action is taken, the fluctuation in the dissolved oxygen content of the water between day and night hinders the uninterrupted growth of the eel.

When the oxygen concentration declines below 1–2 ml/litre eels stick their noses above the water surface and may even die. The minimum acceptable oxygen level is 3 ml/litre. It is easy to rectify an oxygen deficiency in the water or to prevent it and almost all farmers operate electrically driven water wheels as aerators at night and as circulators of oxygen saturated surface water during the daytime. Some Japanese eel farmers find it best to specially partition off a small part of a pond to form a 'pool' and position the water wheel there; this helps the eels to sense where to congregate when the pond oxygen level drops. This technique, however, is not common in Taiwan. There, a few innovative eel farmers have installed compressed air blowers at the bottom of the ponds to increase the oxygen supply. Alternatively, the oxygen level can be simply raised by increasing the rate of water-flow through a pond.

The consumption of oxygen by eels varies under different conditions. Naturally, it increases as the water temperature rises and the mobility of eels improves as shown in Table 15.

Table 15 – Eels oxygen consumption per kg/hour

Temperature (°C)	ml/kg/hour
8	40
16	45
22	57
25	60
30	94

The amount of oxygen required by elvers is considerably higher than that for eels as much higher stocking densities are observed. Without exception a continuous flow of water and compressed air is maintained through elver ponds at all times. Fish in general, when kept together, consume less oxygen than they would if they were kept separately. Eel merchants manage to keep a large number of eels together in tanks, provided they are put in gradually and not simultaneously. Eels can survive for some time out of water as long as their skin remains moist as they can absorb about three-fifths of their total oxygen requirement through their skin.

Pond Waste

Decomposing dead plankton, remnants of feed and eel excrement on the pond base represent another important part of the environment the eel farmer must control. One of the products of decay and decomposition is ammonia which, in the absence of sufficient oxygen, causes eels discomfort and to lose their appetites.

Accumulated waste should be removed from the pond base annually before allowing it to dry out and liming it to promote the decomposition of organic matter in the following year.

Pond Water

Eel ponds require plenty of fresh water and should be located in areas where there is good supply, both quantitatively and qualitatively. In Taiwan and Japan most of the eel ponds use groundwater from deep wells, although irrigation water is also used in some parts. Irrigation water is not desirable because it may be polluted, particularly with pesticides. Underground water should be aerated by spraying or agitation before use.

Sulphur

In ponds containing salt there is usually a large amount of sulphate which produces hydrogen sulphide as a result of the work of sulphate-reducing bacteria. If hydrogen sulphide is produced when the eels are sticking their noses up through lack of oxygen, then the damage will be larger. However, if the water contains iron, then hydrogen sulphide is no problem as it forms iron sulphide. Alternatively, the emergence of hydrogen sulphide from the bottom of the pond can be prevented by scattering ferric oxide into the pond every few weeks.

Nitrogen, Phosphate and Potassium

NP and K are necessary for the multiplication of phytoplankton, and a new pond is fertilised at the very beginning of eel pond culture. The optimum target level for nitrogen is 12.7 ppm, for phosphate 1.3 ppm and potassium 0.1 ppm. Waste products from the eel, feed and phytoplankton, once culture has started, provide sufficient nitrogen and phosphate to make further fertilisation unnecessary in most cases. Research shows that the amount of nitrogen in the water is smaller, while the amount of phosphate tends to be larger, when compound feed is used.

POND DESIGN AND EQUIPMENT

Every eel farmer, like any other farmer, has his own ideas on what he considers to be the best design and layout of his farming area to which he rigidly adheres. In many instances, the layout he has adopted is a modification of previously existing system within the physical confines and limitations of his farm. It is, therefore, possible only to talk in very general terms about the basic physical requirements of an eel farm and to give a number of examples of layouts which a would-be eel farmer is well-advised to adjust and modify to suit his own environment. Any farm design should include three types of ponds namely, elver ponds or tanks; fingerling ponds; and fattening ponds which, of course, correspond to the different stages in an eel's development. In addition, facilities for storing feed, nets and other types of supplementary equipment must also be provided.

Pond Area

The figures for culture pond area are limited to the Far East, as this is the only part of the world where there are appreciable numbers of eel ponds at the present time though, as previously mentioned, increasing numbers of experimental culture farms are in process of development elsewhere. They are, however, not included in these figures as they have, as yet, a negligible commercial output.

A comprehensive breakdown of the distribution and area of eel ponds in Taiwan was provided in the results of a survey carried out in January 1972 and are shown in Table 16.

The figures for nursery ponds refer to those ponds used for rearing elvers to stocking size and do not include intensive elver tanks. Some eel farmers in Taiwan specialise in raising elvers to various sizes and then selling them to other farmers to be grown on to market size.

Table 16 – Area of culture ponds in Taiwan

County	Rearing ponds (ha)	Nursery ponds (ha)	Total (ha)
Changhua	212	—	212
Pingtung	198	10	208
Ilan	49	68	117
Yunlin	70	23	93
Chiayi	44	20	64
Taoyuan	44	11	55
Hsinchu	16	7	23
Others	50	10	60
TOTAL AREA	683	149	832

The rapid growth rate of the Taiwanese eel industry is clearly demonstrated in Table 17 which shows the annual increase in the total area of eel farms. In the last seven years since 1966, the area devoted to eel culture has increased by 20 times. The figures also show the larger size of the Japanese eel industry. As an estimate the the total pond area used for eel culture in Japan and Taiwan in 1973 was nearly 4,000 hectares or 10,000 acres.

Table 17 – Eel pond area in Taiwan and Japan

Year	Number of hectares	
	JAPAN	TAIWAN
1966	1,830	60
1967	—	80
1968	2,272	—
1969	2,089	200
1971	—	660
1972	—	1,058
1973	2,663	1,200

Shizouka Prefecture is the main eel producing Prefecture in Japan, and out of a total area of 2,272 hectares in 1968 it accounted for 1,317 hectares, whereas Achi Prefecture eel ponds covered 540 hectares, Mie Prefecture 163 hectares, and other Prefectures 252 hectares.

Elver Tanks and Ponds

The pond water temperature is a vital factor determining the growth rate of elvers and this one factor exerts the most influence on the type of elver culture tank and pond a farmer adopts. The outside pond water temperature in Japan between December and April is considerably colder than that in Taiwan and, as a result, the Japanese build greenhouses fitted with boilers and steam pipes over their elver ponds, whereas the Taiwanese generally do not.

Elver Tanks

The size of elver tanks, as their name implies, are small in comparison to elver ponds and they may have a water surface area of only 10 sq. metres, measuring 2 metres wide by 5 metres long and 1 metre deep. Smaller sized tanks enable the management and supervision of individual tanks to be considerably improved at the important beginning point of an eel's growth. The bases of the tanks are lined with concrete and slope towards a central drainage point. The tanks can, therefore, be easily washed down and disinfected between batches of elvers being raised. Borehole water is sprayed into the tank either with or without being heated from an overhead pipe which increases the level of aeration. In addition, compressed air from a 2 hp pump is pumped through piping laid on the tank base. Under such a system the flow rate of water and air is very high, with the water being changed every 30 minutes. Generally, the water level in the tank is shallow – only 20–30 cm deep. The feeding area is shaded with wooden boarding and a light hung over this point to attract elvers towards it. A retaining lip is built round the edge of the tank to prevent elvers which are light in weight from climbing up the wall and escaping. An attempt to escape would usually be made during heavy rains, so in most

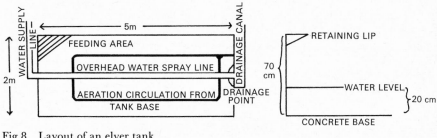

Fig 8   Layout of an elver tank

instances elver tanks are covered by a shed roof and this has an additional advantage in that they are protected from the stresses of direct sunlight. Elver tanks are more frequently found in Taiwan than in Japan, where elver ponds with artificial heating are preferred.

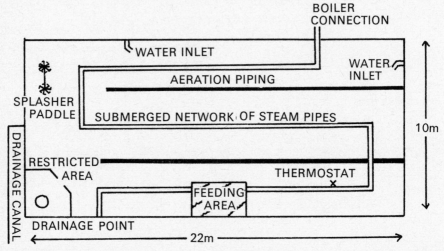

Fig 9   Design of an elver pond

Elver Ponds

The area of the elver pond in Fig 9 is 220 sq metres having measurements of 22 × 10 × 1 m and is considerably larger than an elver tank. In this instance, a retaining lip may or may not be built round the edge of the pond, depending on the size of elvers to be placed in it. The climbing instinct and ability to climb generally ceases once elvers or fingerling eels reach 15 cm in length. Mud forms the pond base so as to reduce costs and as elvers are more hardy by this stage there is no need to exert such stringent hygiene controls.

In outline, elver ponds are basically an enlarged form of elver tanks. A large steel frame greenhouse structure lined with perspex sheeting is built over the ponds and the storage and boiler areas. Along one side of the greenhouse runs a drain to dispose of used pond water. Borehole water is heated by oil-fired boilers and the resultant steam passed through a network of pipes positioned just above the pond base. A thermostat positioned in the water records the temperature and regulates the flow of steam, as this is in part dependant on how much direct sunlight is heating the greenhouse and hence the water during the daytime.

Half the pond water is changed daily with borehole water being introduced into the pond from a number of inlet pipes raised above the water surface and positioned some distance away from the drainage point, so as to improve the circulation of water round the pond. Water is generally pumped out of the pond and may be taken from a restricted area rather than be allowed to freely overflow. Water aeration is improved either by splasher paddles or by plastic piping laid on the pond base through which compressed air is blown. Feed, as in elver tanks, is offered from under a covered area in baskets.

As can be imagined, such a layout is very expensive costing anything up to £30,000 or more to cover and equip an area of 600 sq metres. This is a high level of capital outlay considering these facilities are used only for a few months of the year. A number of farmers reduce costs by not adopting quite such an elaborate system. They replace the steel framework with tubular piping, cut down on size and replace perspex sheeting with plastic sheeting. In some instances they may rely solely on the sun to heat the water through the sheeting rather than use oil-fired boilers.

Fingerling Ponds

The pond area allocated per eel increases as they grow from elvers to fingerling eels. The average area of each fingerling pond varies between 400–600 sq metres. The pond base is lined with mud, sand and stones, and is inclined away from the sides as Fig 10 shows. (Fig 10 overpage) No underwater aeration points are used with all the eels' oxygen needs being met by splasher paddles. Water enters in one side of the pond and drains out the other. A retaining lip may be built round the edge as a precaution though, at this stage, it is mostly unnecessary. The water is 80–100 cm deep.

Fattening Ponds

In the early days of commercial eel culture in Japan fattening ponds had large surface areas of water, of up to 6,000–10,000 sq metres or more. However, today, the tendency is towards smaller ponds based on the principle that 'it is unwise to have all your eggs in one basket' in case disease strikes and smaller ponds can mean better management. In Japan, the average fattening pond size is now 2,000–3,000 sq metres. In Taiwan, they tend to

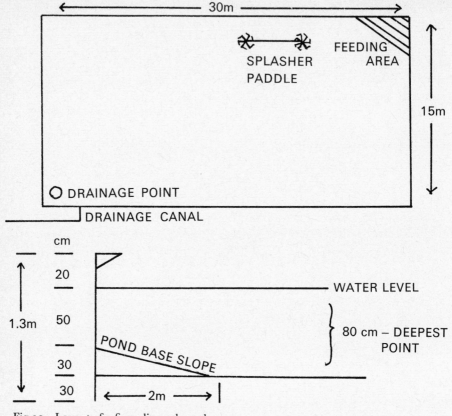

Fig 10   Layout of a fingerling eel pond

be nearer 1,000 sq metres or even smaller. Fattening ponds for running water culture are, as a rule, smaller than ponds for still-water culture.

A fattening pond is an enlarged version of a fingerling eel pond in much the same way as an elver pond is a magnified elver tank. There are very few differences between these two types of pond. It is, however, worth going into detail about the construction of fattening ponds and many of the points made now can equally well be applied to fingerling eel ponds.

The pond depth is 80–100 cm and its wall is constructed from either bricks, stones or moulded concrete slabs. The latter are becoming increasingly popular as they are easy to mould and slot into position round the side of the pond at a slightly inclined angle.

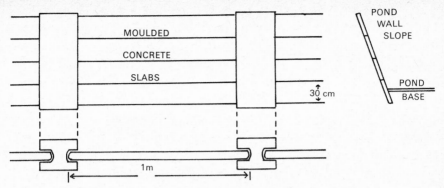

Fig 11   Pond wall of concrete slabs and their angle of slope

It is advisable when constructing a pond to slope the pond base towards the drainage point. Firstly, this has the obvious advantage that water can be quickly drained from the pond, and secondly, it helps congregate eels in one area at harvest time. Most ponds, therefore, slope both at the edges and towards the drainage point.

Various drainage systems are adopted which depend on either gravity or a pump being operated. If pond water is gravity drained, then water flows through a series of retaining boards used to regulate the pond water height and to keep eels in the pond. Fig 12 illustrates the layout of a drainage point (Fig 12 overpage). Only a limited amount of water flows out of a pond in the still-water culture system and this rate can be easily controlled. Some systems allow water to flow out through a pipe at the base of the drainage point. This is advantageous at harvest time as a bag can be placed over the pipe and eels easily collected. Alternatively, water can be pumped out of a pond using a 2–3 hp motor to raise water into a central drainage canal.

This motor is not run continuously as the flow rate in still-water ponds is relatively low, so when the water pump is not operating, surplus water drains slowly out through an overflow pipe.

Sun shades, other than those placed over the feeding area, are rarely used even though the water temperature may get quite high. This is because the functioning of the phytoplankton would be interfered with, as they depend on sunlight. The feeding area consists of a wooden structure measuring 3 m × 2 m and 1 m high, the bottom of which reaches just below the water surface. This framework has a hatch through which feed is placed into a

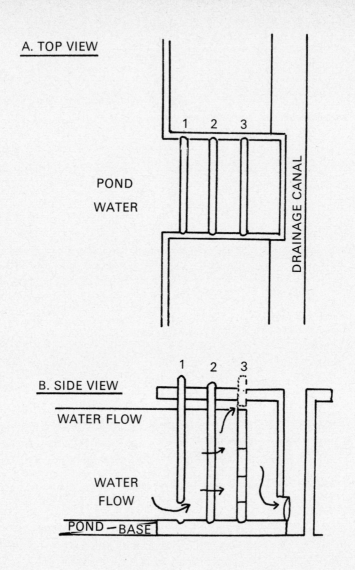

A. TOP VIEW

1 2 3

POND

WATER

DRAINAGE CANAL

B. SIDE VIEW

1 2 3

WATER FLOW

WATER
FLOW

POND — BASE

1 = SLUICE BOARD

2 = SIEVE BOARD — RETAINS EELS

3 = MONK GATE — CONTROLS WATER LEVEL

Fig 12   Construction of a drainage gate – note 1, 2, 3

basket suspended from cross-supports. The feeding area is usually situated near a splasher paddle or on that side of a pond most exposed to the wind so that the level of aeration in this area can be increased at feeding time when a high concentration of eels accumulate in one small area.

Mention has been made earlier of the use of 'pools' in Japan as a method to enable eels to identify where oxygen enriched water is available at times when it is deficient in other areas of the pond. The use of 'pools' is not widespread in Taiwan and providing an adequate number of splashers are used, they become unnecessary. Most ponds in Taiwan have two or more splashers each. A pool as Fig 13 shows, can either be positioned where a water inlet is located or be built round a splasher.

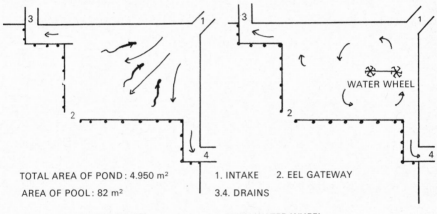

TOTAL AREA OF POND: 4.950 m²   1. INTAKE   2. EEL GATEWAY

AREA OF POOL: 82 m²   3.4. DRAINS

A. WITHOUT WATER WHEEL   B. WITH WATER WHEEL

Fig 13   Structure of an eel pool with and without water wheel

Splasher paddles or water wheels are very simple structures usually powered by a small electric 1–2 hp motor driving two axles which revolve the paddles at up to 150 times a minute. The whole unit is fixed to poles and secured to floats which rise and fall with the level of the pond water. Care should be taken not to expose the cable carrying the electric current to the splasher and it is best buried in the ground.

The diagrams used to outline different types of ponds and tanks discussed in this section have been shown in isolation. Fig 14 shows the complete layout of a possible eel farm and the interrelationship between different types of ponds.

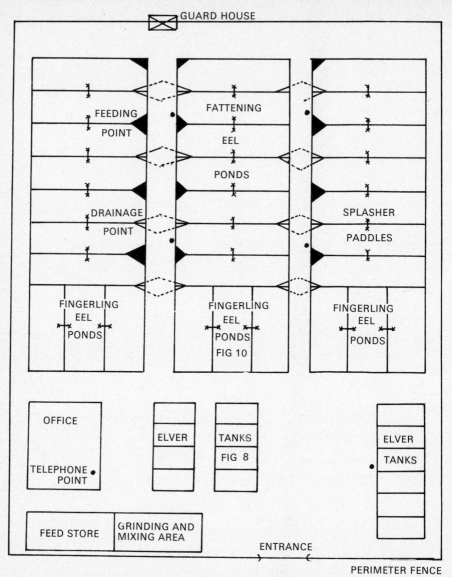

GUARD HOUSE

FEEDING POINT

FATTENING

EEL

PONDS

DRAINAGE POINT

SPLASHER

PADDLES

FINGERLING EEL PONDS

FINGERLING EEL PONDS

FIG 10

FINGERLING EEL PONDS

OFFICE

TELEPHONE POINT

ELVER

TANKS

FIG 8

ELVER

TANKS

FEED STORE

GRINDING AND MIXING AREA

ENTRANCE

PERIMETER FENCE

Fig 14   Layout of an eel-culture farm (not to scale)

The ideal ponds used at any one stage of development are uniform in size as this helps to produce an even size fattened product,
besides aiding calculations on correct stocking densities and feeding levels. In Taiwan, some ponds are constructed above ground

(with the bottom on ground level) to facilitate drainage and to save the cost of excavation. However, ponds using irrigation as opposed to borehole water have to be built below the level of the irrigation canals. One or two ponds in an eel farm may purposely be kept empty of eels though filled with water, in case it is necessary to hurriedly transfer eels from one pond to another when a change in water quality or a disease outbreak occurs.

SUPPLEMENTARY EQUIPMENT

The construction and design of different types of eel ponds and tanks has been outlined in the previous section. One of the subjects which is often overlooked in literature on culture is the type of supplementary equipment a farmer needs to purchase in order to successfully run an eel farm. This may include equipment and facilities needed for feeding and handling eels and for general pond management and security.

Feeding

An eel farmer should provide himself with adequate facilities to enable him to store sufficient feedingstuffs and vitamin oils under cover throughout the year. In this way, he can reap some of the financial benefits to be gained from bulk buying and from buying out of season. Compound feeds, partly because of their high protein content, are becoming increasingly expensive so wastage of them must be kept to a minimum. The feed storage building should be weather-proof and generally it is advantageous to keep the feed bags stacked on pallets or raised platforms in case of sudden flood conditions.

A grinding machine is essential if raw or frozen fish are being fed to eels at some stage of their feeding programme. Generally, most farmers only buy in the amount of raw fish they are likely to use straight away rather than go to the expense of building, maintaining and running cold storage facilities. Fish, such as mackerel, are delivered to a farm in 10–15 kg paper bound bundles and simply stacked at the side of a shed until required. A small platform is built round the input point of a grinding machine so as to speed up the rate of operation and to avoid having wet fish sliding all over the floor. A small water boiler may also be available if it is the practice of the farm to feed whole fish on strings to eels.

continued on p 97

Fig 13 An electric motor on a dividing wall between two ponds can power two splasher wheels the same time. Note how narrow the dividing wall is.

Fig 14 A splasher paddle at rest on floats secured by poles.

Fig 15 A splasher paddle churning up water, and increasing the aeration level.

Fig 16 A switch panel between ponds controls the splasher paddles and provides telephone contact with the main office. In the background a 2m fence keeps intruders out.

Fig 17 A water drainage canal runs alongside the elver tanks, and water flows in through the top pipes.

Fig 18 Tanks have retaining lips around the top edge to prevent elvers from escaping. Water is sprayed down into the tanks from overhead pipes suspended across the tanks.

Fig 19 A compressor pump is used to continuously aerate elver tanks.

Fig 20 The level of water aeration is increased by blowing air through small holes in piping resting on the bottom of elver tanks.

Fig 21 A simple greenhouse framework (with polythene removed) covers an elver rearing pond in Japan.

Fig 22 A massive costly high roof greenhouse covering a large elver pond water area.

Fig 23 The outside of a well built elver pond greenhouse. A water drainage canal runs along the side wall.

Fig 24 Three elver ponds are covered by this greenhouse. The pond walls are made from concrete blocks, and water inlet pipes protrude over the pond.

Fig 25 Newly captured elvers are trained to take food from below a covered area at the edge of the pond.

Fig 26 Steam pipes are laid out over the pond base to increase the water temperature, and to initiate an earlier start to the growing season. Splasher paddles aerate the water.

Fig 27 Elver pond bases slope towards the drainage point, where the few remaining eels can be easily caught.

Fig 28 Water is lifted and pumped out into a canal running alongside the greenhouse. A gauze mesh cover prevents elvers from being sucked out.

Fig 29 Water freely flows out at a
drainage point to maintain the pond
water level at a predetermined height.

Fig 30 Water drains along a canal
beneath wooden slats on the dividing wall
between fattening ponds.

Fig 31 An electric water pump is
connected to an outlet point and water
pumped out of the pond when necessary.
Note the retaining lip round the pond
wall edge.

Fig 32 The final bit of water in a pond is
often removed by pump, when no more
will drain by gravity.

Fig 33 A raised brick wall eel farm in Taiwan. Some eel culture farm ponds are built above ground level, rather than excavated.

Fig 34 Small elver rearing tanks are built at the side of the main culture pond.

Fig 35 Borehole water is raised by pumps to run along canals at the edge of the ponds.

Fig 36 At the end of the season water is pumped into a central drainage canal. During the season a controlled amount of water flows into the canal through a drainage gate.

Fig 37 Water flowing down a central canal into an eel fattening pond, next to a guard's house.

Fig 38 Feed area shelters can be cheaply built by nailing a few odd bits of wood together.

Fig 39 Covered elver tanks on a Taiwanese eel farm.

Fig 40 An eerie sight! A Taiwanese eel farmhouse surrounded on all sides by fattening ponds.

Fig 41 The compound feed;—oil and water mix are tipped into bowls out of the mixer.

Fig 42 Fish and silkworm pupae are minced before being added to the eel's diet.

Fig 43 Seine nets used to catch eels are hung up in a shed to dry after use.

Fig 44 Feed ingredients are carefully weighed before mixing.

Fig 45 Accumulated pond mud is laboriously removed from the bottom. Note the security fence in the background.

Fig 46 At the end of a season ponds are emptied, and limed. Note how the pond bottom slopes at the edges.

Fig 47 Different sized eels fall between the wooden slat gaps, as eels are regularly subdivided.

Fig 48 Moulded close fitting concrete blocks are easily handled for building effective pond walls.

94

Fig 49 Experimental elver culture tanks at the Shizouka Fisheries Experimental Station. Japan.

Fig 50 A close up view of an experimental elver culture tank showing brackish and freshwater inlets, covered feeding area; and drainage point.

Fig 51 Main water drainage canal dividing experimental culture tanks.

Fig 52 Aeration unit and flexible pipe lines supplying experimental eel fattening ponds.

Fig 53 Eels cornered in a gill net are transferred by eel scoop net into a collection container.

Fig 54 Eel farm workers slowly drawing a seine net across a pond to capture fattened eels.

Fig 55 Fattened cultured eels ready for market are held in a well aerated tank for 2–3 days to discharge all their gut content.

Fig 56 Live eels are packed in a sealed oxygenated polythene bag, and cardboard boxes for market.

Compound feeds are usually fed in multiples of bags and the only item of equipment required for feed preparation is a simple mixing machine which should be large enough to take 50–60 kg of feed at any one time. Water, oil and compound feed are added to the mixer, mixed and then tipped out of the mixing bowl and poured into large basins. Each pond has its own numbered basin so that the right quantity of feed is fed to the right pond. The proportion of oil, water and compound feed used is not a hit and miss affair; compound feed and water are carefully weighed out on scales and the oil measured in a flask before they are mixed together.

Handling

Eel capture can be carried out in a number of ways. The most easy and effective way is to scoop eels out of the pond with a net at feeding time when the concentration of fish in any one area of the pond is at its greatest. Ninety-five per cent of the stock can be captured this way. Alternatively, as eel ponds are relatively shallow, a weighted seine net operated by a number of men wading in the water can be used to drive eels into one corner before they are scooped out. Naturally, any fish farm equipment includes a number of seine nets the dimension of which are dependent on the pond area in question. Pond drainage for the capture of eels follows the same basic principle as a seine net in that pond water is drained out to such an extent that the water available to eels is gradually reduced to a point when they can be easily scooped out.

Eel handling equipment is required either to transfer stock from pond to pond or to capture eels prior to grading and or marketing. Smaller sized eels are usually graded by using a range of wooden boxes with different width gaps on the bottom, the larger eels being retained and the smaller ones fall through.

Table 18 – Gap sizes through which different eels will fall

Gap size (mm)	Size of eel escaping (gm)
7	7
9	13
11	19
13	37

D

Larger sized eels weighing more than 100 gms are normally graded on sorting tables. The captured eels are released down a central canal on the table from where a number of graders pick out the different sized eels and transfer them to baskets.

A live eel is, of course, a particularly difficult fish to handle being very slimy and slippery. Inwardly sloping plastic baskets with close-fitting lids are used to transfer captured eels from pond to pond. These have an obvious advantage in that because of their shape an eel cannot escape from them and in that a smooth plastic surface is unlikely to damage the eel's skin and does not provide a surface up which an eel can climb.

Pond Management Equipment

The more important types of equipment required for pond management are those used on a day to day basis to measure changes in the chemical composition of the pond water, such as pH, oxygen content and the presence and build up of specific elements which can have a damaging effect on an eel's health. An eel farmer, more and more has to be a specialist who can accurately monitor everything occurring on his farm. A small suitably equipped laboratory is an essential if basic disease identification and water analysis readings are to be carried out.

Annually, at the end of the season, ponds are drained and left to dry out in the sun over a period of time. The practice on a number of farms is to scrape the top few centimetres of pond mud off and laboriously dispose of it elsewhere before relining the base with fresh earth. The cleansing of ponds helps remove eel excrement, feed and other waste and decomposed products, as so to reduce the likelihood of disease being carried over from one season into the next. A farm, therefore, needs a number of shovels and containers to be able to carry waste out of the ponds.

Alternatively, when stones form the pond base, because they are not so easy to remove, farmers lime the pond. Storage facilities should include an area for keeping bags of lime.

Security

Eel flesh is highly priced and in an extremely competitive business acts of sabotage are frequent. In most cases it is all too easy to drain ponds of water so as to make the eels or elvers irretrievable.

Therefore, incredible as it may seem, many eel farms now, for security reasons, have high wire fences all the way round the perimeter of the ponds, with barbed wire on the top. Entrance to the farm may be limited to one gate only on which a guard is positioned throughout the season. He is in direct contact by telephone with the main farm office and can summon help immediately as and when necessary.

In addition, a number of farms have further telephones strategically placed so that help can be summoned from any area. These telephones are also used to call for help when a checker on a routine management tour of the ponds notices something is wrong with the water or with the eels. It cannot be emphasised too strongly that there is a definite need to provide adequate facilities to protect ponds from malicious intruders and this does not only apply to the Far East. Poachers in one form or another are found worldwide.

In summary, a check list of supplementary equipment facilities should include, a store for feed, fertiliser, nets, packaging equipment, a water boiler, grinding and mixing equipment, feed bowls. scales, shovels, eel carrier baskets, and a laboratory for water analysis and disease identification.

EXPERIMENTAL CULTURE PONDS

The true value of a book such as this is not to be found solely in outlining what to do or what not to do to farmers already practising eel farming but to stimulate an increased interest in eel culture and to provide some guidelines for those who are not at present culturing eels in different parts of the world. Those people may include private individuals, commercial organisations or Government Departments with a responsibility for the development of aquaculture. It is all very well to read about the different approaches to fish farming but the real test comes when putting a theory or an idea into practice.

It is impossible to outline all the possible ways of eel farming so as to cover all eventualities. One can only suggest that the data included here is adopted according to local environment. Many of the systems outlined are those practised commercially in Japan and Taiwan. A very necessary first step is to adjust these systems to a particular environment which requires experimentation. No attempt should be made to build a full-scale eel farm, until a bank of accumulated information has been built up relevant to the area in which it is intended to farm.

This section outlines experimental eel culture ponds varying from aquaria to a scaled-down version of a large eel fattening pond. Much of the data included is taken from experimental eel stations in Japan and Taiwan and it is hoped it will provide a useful guideline. No attempt is made to define what experiments should be carried out as these depend so much on individual knowledge and ideas. This includes the response of a particular species of eel to different types of feed, stocking densities, local diseases and many other factors.

Aquaria

The most popular type of experimental aquaria used in Japan is one made of polyvinyl chloride and measures 20 × 20 × 50 cm. Well water is supplied at the rate of 0.5 to 0.7 litres per minute to these tanks simulating flowing water culture conditions, via an overhead pipe and through a tap, which can be regulated. The water is preheated to 25 °C and aerated before being passed into the tanks. Several tanks are lined up side by side along a bench and water flows out through an adjustable overflow point into a

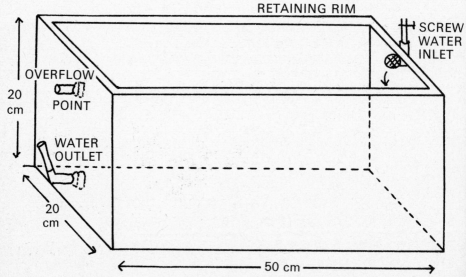

Fig 15   Design of an experimental aquarium

trough running in front of each tank. A narrow rim at the top of
the tank prevents elvers from escaping and nets over the inlet,
outlet and overflow points serve the same purpose.

30–35 elvers are placed in an aquarium for each experiment.
These are accustomed to feeding before an experiment begins
and generally weigh 2.5 g each. Experimental elvers are fed twice
daily except on Saturdays and Sundays, when they are fed once.
A paste diet is extruded into a tank from a 50 ml nylon syringe
without a needle and the remainder of the diet and faeces siphoned
out 30 minutes after each feeding. Fish are weighed individually at
2-week intervals by anaesthetizing with a 1.2% urethan solution.

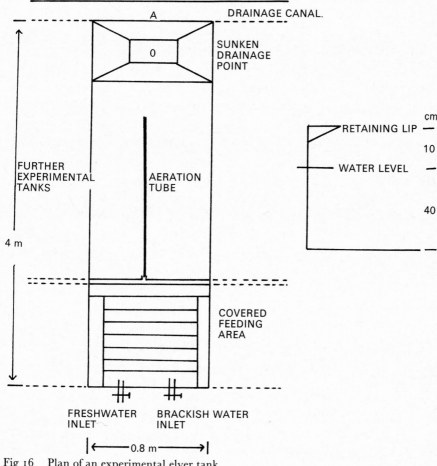

Fig 16   Plan of an experimental elver tank

Elver Tanks

The diagrams used to illustrate the design of experimental elver tanks, fingerling and fattening ponds, are taken from the Shizouka Fisheries Experimental Station, Japan. A design feature of the elver tanks, shown in Fig 16, is the inclusion of facilities to enable either fresh or brackish water, or any combination of the two, to be pumped into the tanks. The feeding area is covered by boards from which a feeding basket is suspended. Additional aeration is provided by underwater pipes to supplement the water oxygen content. Water is drained out through a guarded overflow pipe into a canal running alongside the tanks. The water depth in the tanks is 40 cm and an overhanging ledge restricts the upward movement of elvers. The area of each tank is just over three square metres and each has an easily cleanable concrete base.

Fingerling Ponds

The same basic design is used for fingerling ponds as for elver tanks, the only difference between them being size. Fingerling ponds measure up to 1 × 8 × 1 m each.

Fattening Ponds

Both brackish and fresh water can be run into the fattening ponds and for all intents and purposes, as one would expect, the experimental ponds are scaled down versions of commercial eel ponds each having its own feeding area, splasher paddles, and water outlets. Fig 17 outlines the size and design of an experimental fattening pond. It will be noted additional aeration facilities are provided. The water level is 80 cm deep and there is a small rim round the edge of the pond.

PRODUCTION AND MANAGEMENT OF EELS

The sections on eel feed and pond design and equipment, have hinted at much of the data included in this section. It brings together a number of aspects of eel farming and outlines important day to day managerial points, also some of the production targets which need to be set.

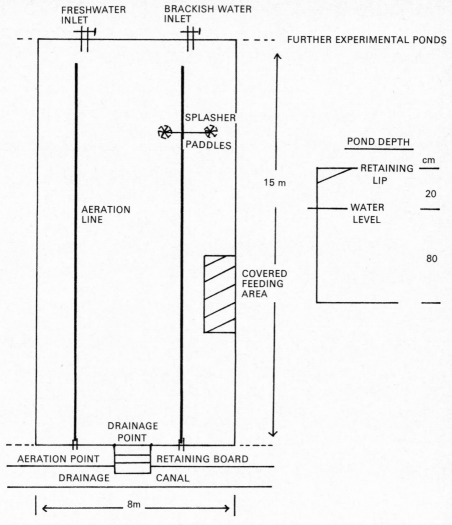

Fig 17 Design for an experimental fattening pond

Stocking Density

Stocking densities can be expressed either in terms of weight or number of eels per unit area. Often the two approaches appear to be in conflict with one another as they depend so much on which culture system has been adopted. The different types of ponds listed in Table 19 refers to those previously outlined.

Table 19 – Pond stocking densities

Type of pond	Dimensions (m)	Area (m^2)	kg/pond-IN	Number/kg-OUT
Elver tank	2.5 × 4	10	3.5	1,500–2,000
Fingerling pond	10 × 40	400	100–150	100
Fattening pond	33 × 20	660	300@100/kg or 900@30/kg	5

There are 6,000 Japanese elvers each weighing 0.17 g in a kilogramme, so when a 10 sq metre elver tank is stocked 3.5 kg. × 6,000 elvers are placed in it, (a rate of over 2,000 elvers or 400 g of elvers per square metre). This is an extremely high stocking density, and further emphasises the comments made already about the need to maintain a constant high level of aeration and water change in the tanks. A certain minimum stocking density is required to promote growth. There is evidence that elvers do not grow as well if there is a low population density.

Elvers will have nearly trebled in weight after about two months from their introduction into heated elver tanks. The tanks are now overstocked and it is necessary to transfer elvers into the larger elver ponds. 100 kg of elvers with 1,500 in each kilo, (or 150,000 fingerling eels) are released into a 400 sq metre fingerling eel pond. The stocking rate is about 400 eels or 100 g of fingerling eels per square metre.

As eels grow they are periodically captured and divided according to their size, before being released into a new pond. The selection is carried out by catching them at feeding time and is wholly necessary if eels are to be cultured successfully and a rapid rate of growth of individual fish is to be ensured. The more frequently eels are selected, as a rule, the more rapidly they will grow.

The final stage of growth and development is carried out in fattening ponds. Here 300 kg of eels weighing 10 g each at the rate of 100 in each kilo (or 30,000 eels) are released in 660 sq metres of surface water at the rate of 50–60 eels per square metre. The final production target is to produce an eel weighing 150/200 g.

Growth Rates

The growth rate of Japanese eels in the first year is summarised in Table 20. These eels were not grown in boiler heated water and naturally in the absence of such a system, growth rates are much reduced. A number of farmers claim it is possible, under a water-heated system, to produce some 150/200 g eels in 7–9 months which is a considerable improvement on the figures given below.

Table 20 – Average growth rate of eels in first year

	g		g
February	0.18	July	5.48
March	0.30	August	15.00
May	0.64	October	23.00
June	2.72	November	29.00

Under a more traditional approach to eel culture, the fattening process takes two years to complete and a 30–40 g fingerling eel is the target weight to be reached by the end of the first year. This means a 150/200 fold increase in weight in such a period of time. Growth rates, as might be expected, are not uniform unless frequent dividing is practised. Some eels may weigh as little as 2 g, and others as much as 120 g by the end of the year. The growth of smaller eels is inhibited by larger eels. High mortality rates occur in the first 3–4 months of culture, unless there is very close supervision. These deaths may be due to some elvers not being sufficiently well-trained to accept feed and to disease outbreaks.

There is no difference in growth rates between male and female eels, up until the 40 cm size. Thereafter, the growth rate of males decreases, and in particular those of the European eel.

Fig 18 shows the European male eel's growth rate slows down considerably at a length of 40 cm, and that it reaches a maximum length of 50 cm, or a weight of 100–120 g. In contrast, the European and Japanese female eels grow up to 50–70 cm in length and reach a body weight of 300–500 g in Japanese culture ponds. The ratio between both male and female European and Japanese eels is as high as 20:1 in favour of the males, with its resultant adverse effect on eel growth rates. A considerable amount of research is under way to improve growth rates by the introduc-

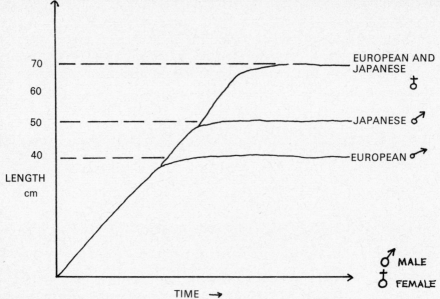

Fig 18   Difference in growth rates between male and female European and Japanese eels

tion of female growth hormones into the diet, the results of which are spectacular. The sex of an eel is determined at the 14–20 cm size. Up until this stage the gonads carry both male and female cells, thereafter one or the other is distinguishable.

Yield

The acceptable market size of an eel cultured in Japan is between 150 and 200 g and the target production figure per square metre of fattening pond water area under the still-water culture system is 4 kilogrammes of eels per annum. This figure can also be expressed as twenty 200 g eels per annum in this area of water, or 40 tons of eel per hectare. Production figures are so dependent on the level of farm management under consideration that some farms may claim to produce up to 8 kg per sq metre, while others produce as little as or less than 1 kg per sq metre.

A number of farms, however, specialise in the production of fingerling eels and sell them to other farmers, known as 'Futo' farmers, who in turn specialise in producing fattened eels. The main objective of a fingerling eel farm is to produce 10–40 g eels as quickly as possible for resale for stocking purposes. These farmers play the market and release eels for sale when prices are favourable between June and early autumn.

Table 21 outlines the annual turnover of an eel farm in terms of input of elvers and feeding stuffs as well as output of fattened eels. The figures given refer to 1968, since when there have been considerable improvements in productivity and efficiency on eel farms. This particular farm was feeding raw fish and not compound feeds. There was 1 hectare of ponds, dividing into 4 ponds respectively of 5000 m^2; 3300 m^2; 10,000 m^2 and 700 m^2 and facilities included four sets of 3 hp motors; four sets of 2 hp watermills: two wells; and two sets of 2 hp vertical pumps.

Table 21 – Turnover of eel culture farm

	Amount (kg)	Unit price (yen)	Total (yen '000)
Amount stocked	280	4,000	1,120
Amount harvested	5,600	750	4,200
Feed	48,000	30	1,440
Running expenses	—	—	1,000
		Gross income	1,760

The annual output of Japanese eel farmers is shown in Table 22. By comparison, the catch of wild eels totalled 3,200 tons in 1969, or 12% of the total weight of eels marketed in that country. In the same year the estimated total area of culture ponds in Japan was 2,089 hectares which produced 23,300 tons of eel. Analysis of these figures reveals that average yield per square metre in the whole country was a little over 1 kilo after having taken into account variations in farming practice and disease outbreaks.

Table 22 – Annual production of cultured eels in Japan ('000 tons)

1953	2.5	1968	23.6
1955	3.6	1969	23.3
1957	5.7	1970	16.7
1961	8.1	1971	14.2
1963	9.9	1972	14.1
1965	16.0	1973	15.2
1966	17.0	1974	17.1
1967	19.6		

In Taiwan in 1973, it was estimated there was a total of 1,200 hectares of pond area which produced 10,000 tons. These figures indicate the average annual production level per square metre is still in the region of 1 kilogramme of fattened eels, or 10 tons per hectare. It should be remembered that these pond area figures include both nursery and fattening ponds.

The theoretically possible production figure from a kilogramme of elvers is nearly one ton. This assumes there are 6,000 elvers in a kilogramme, a survival rate of 80% is achieved and each survivor is fattened to 200 g. This figure indicates theory is a long way ahead of practice.

Day to day Pond Management

The golden rule of any aquaculture management is prevention is better than cure. Stunted elvers or eels carrying any fungul growths are always removed immediately from a pond. Slow growing eels are also removed and culling, as has been emphasised time and again, is done frequently.

Management checks are made daily of the water pH; the maximum and minimum water temperature; the level of phytoplankton by submerging a white disc into the water; and the water oxygen level. A regular patrol of the ponds is made a number of times throughout the day.

A careful check is kept on the number and weight of eels in each pond. Every two weeks a sample is weighed and the total weight in a pond calculated. Records control the amount of feed fed and the amount left over.

Harvesting and Selection of Eels

There are four main methods of harvesting cultured eels which have been outlined in the section on supplementary equipment. Firstly, a seine net is used when the condition of the pond water is not good and the eels do not show any appetite to gather for feeding. Secondly, a gill net measuring about 4 × 4 m is used, three sides of which are stiffened by bamboo with the fourth side free and made to droop with small lead weights. Thirdly, a scoop net can be used at feeding time, and fourthly a pond can be drained. This method is practised mainly in winter when the entire pond is drained. The day for water draining should be warm and windless and if the pond tends to contain salt, oxidised iron is scattered the previous day to prevent toxication by hydrogen sulphide. Drainage should be started early in the morning and after half the water has been drained the drainage water gate should be fully opened while a long tube-like net (about 2.5 m), with a mouth of 50 cm in diameter, is attached to catch eels as they come out. If this is done early in the morning then the eels will not bore into the bed soil but rather swim along with the outgoing water.

Eels are selected for size on a selection table immediately after harvesting either for marketing or returning to a pond.

Table 23 – Eel selection sizes

Weight (g)		Action
Under 120	—	Returned to pond in the summer and in winter kept until the following year.
120–150	—	Marked for shipment to Tokyo.
160–250	—	Marked for shipment to other areas of Japan.
300+	—	Marked for export

The domestic consumption of eels is 50% in Tokyo; 30% in Osaka; and other parts of Japan account for the remaining 20%. In Tokyo, the largest market, the demand for eel flesh has increased annually at the rate of 15% since 1960. This remarkable increase is basically the result of improvement in the general dietary trend and also consumption has been stimulated by the concentration of factories in the producing prefectures, such as Shizouka, where boiled eels in the form of instant foodstuffs are processed.

There is a preference among consumers and retailers for the Japanese eel as this species (as opposed to the European eel) has a lower condition factor in the region of 1.6–1.9; whereas the European eel condition factor is 2.0–2.5, making it less suitable for the preparation of 'kabyaki'.

Pre-Shipment Starvation
This term describes the process of cutting eels off from feed for 3–4 days while they are confined in a limited space before shipment. By doing this, the cushion of fat is reduced, various odours that have been acquired from feeds are removed and the eel will clear

its guts of food so that no faeces are included in the despatched sample. This process contributes directly to improving the quality of eels and at the same time is effective in forcing them to adapt to less oxygen, which is a necessary condition for safe shipment.

Three main methods are used for pre-shipment starvation. Firstly, the elver tanks may be used for this process, where high stocking densities are involved, and exactly the same procedure is observed as for elvers. That is, continued high aeration and a quick rate of water change. Secondly, about 20 kg of selected eels can be put into a basket and hung in a water tank of fresh water, or well water pumped up for that purpose. Thirdly, 10 baskets each containing 3 kg of eels can be stacked up and the eels showered with water from the top.

By the end of the process eels fed on a fresh fish diet will have lost 8% of the weight approximately and eels fed on compounds 20%.

Shipment

Eels that have been selected and separated according to weight are put into vinyl bags each containing 10 kg of eels with 1 kg of ice, and a small quantity of oxygen from an oxygen cylinder and closed with a rubber band. Two of these bags are put in a cardboard box and if the destination is reachable within 24 hours, shipment in this way can be carried out without any damage to the eels.

A DECISION AS TO WHETHER OR NOT TO CULTURE EELS?

Introduction

The time is rapidly approaching when man can no longer allow nature to annually provide millions of specimens of rearing stock to migrate upstream and die in vast numbers influenced by natural selection, survival of the fittest and many other factors. Many areas of the world's oceans and seas have been overfished or are becoming increasingly polluted, thereby forcing man either to zealously guard his own territorial waters and to seek an extension of this area or to search further and further afield to satisfy the spiralling demands of an ever-increasing world population. More and more individuals and organisations in Europe and other parts of the world are showing an interest and involvement in intensive fish culture, which the Japanese have long practised as a partial means of alleviating this problem. Eel culture has already made and will continue to make a contribution within this framework, though at present technical, financial and managerial resources have been concentrated principally, so far, on the culture of other species of fish.

There are many practical and financial questions which need to be asked and answered satisfactorily, when analysing the feasibility of investing in and establishing an eel culture farm. The first part of this section considers some of the questions and criteria which must be taken into consideration. Some points mentioned are taken from that excellent book *Farming the Edge of the Sea* by E. S. Iversen. The second part outlines the main fixed and variable capital input items and returns which must be estimated when preparing a budget for a new eel farm enterprise. The figures given refer to data prepared in Taiwan, and must, therefore, be modified and costed locally before application. No commercially viable operations are as yet underway other than in the Far East, so no proven Western cost figures are available. The final part of this section discusses briefly the potential for intensive eel culture and the expansion of extensive eel culture in Europe. Both are development areas for the future. Although much of the discussion in this section concentrates on Europe, many of the points and questions raised are equally applicable to other regions of the world, where organisations and individuals are considering eel culture.

Some criteria and questions

The physical and environmental features of a potential eel culture site need to be carefully assessed and analysed before deciding whether or not they are ideal and before committing financial resources. The following are some of the questions which need to be examined, not necessarily in order of importance.

1. Are adequate suitable sites available within the area to build a sufficient number of culture ponds and supporting facilities such as stores and offices? Access to 3–4 hectares of land per farm is desirable.
2. Can the culture ponds be located so that they can be free drained almost dry? This is not essential if water pumping

equipment is available. The use of gravity, however, reduces the cost of drainage, and aids harvesting. It is not usual in eel culture to allow water to flow from one pond into another. Further in comparison with trout farming, only a relatively low flow rate through the ponds is required. The majority of Far Eastern culture ponds are built on flat ground and are drained independently.

3. Is the substrata suitable for water retention, or must some type of sealant be used? A sandy water retaining pond substrata is advisable for culture based on the promotion of phytoplankton. This aids the breakdown of waste materials and the cleaning of ponds between the culture of different batches of eels.

4. Is there any danger of loss of stock due to storms, flooding and erosion? This seems an obvious consideration and refers not only to the overflow of the ponds, but also to the river near to which the ponds may be located. The mobility of eels at certain stages is activated by the introduction of freshwater and they can easily slide over moist ground surfaces and escape. Eel culture, at the present time, is located in tropical and sub-tropical regions and these are especially vulnerable to heavy sudden downpours which can raise river levels dramatically in a few hours. A careful check should be made on the rainfall and flood data of previous years. A borehole water supply located on the edge of the flood plain may overcome some of these problems.

5. Is there ample sunshine for producing phytoplankton? In freshwater eel culture, phytoplankton normally produce the majority of oxygen consumed by eels, unless some other system for the artificial introduction of oxygen is used. Photosynthesis only takes place in daylight hours and prolonged periods of overcast weather are detrimental. The culture of eels in brackish water is, of course, not dependent on phytoplankton for the production of oxygen.

6. Are there strong winds in the area to improve the water oxygen content? Many eel culture ponds are built deliberately at such an angle as to give the water the maximum possible exposure to the local winds so as to reduce the dependence on phytoplankton and paddle aerators. Too strong a continual

wind can, however, be more of a hindrance than a help by blowing the phytoplankton to one side of a pond and chilling the water. It may be better, in the long run, to artificially control the oxygen content of a pond rather than over-exposing the pond and relying on the prevailing weather conditions.

7. Is there an ample water supply? In tropical and sub-tropical regions river water levels rise and fall seasonally a great deal. Calculations on adequate water supplies must be based on the lowest level of water available in the summer months, plus a sizeable safety margin. The sinking of a suitably deep borehole into the water table should eliminate, to a large extent, the need to trust the river water level. Checks should be made as to whether any prolonged periods of drought have been recorded in the area. The water flow rate through the ponds is deliberately kept relatively low so as to avoid disturbing phytoplankton with sometimes as little as only 5–10% of the total volume being changed daily. Adequate reserves of water should be available if the need arises to quickly and completely change the pond water.

8. Is the prevailing water temperature sufficiently high throughout the year? This is one of the main factors limiting the widespread adoption of eel culture and needs particularly careful and honest analysis. In Europe the water temperature rarely reaches the optimum eel culture level of $25\,^{\circ}C$ for any prolonged period of time. The larger the number of months or days of the year the average water tempeature is naturally heated to $25\,^{\circ}C$, the better the site. There are, at present, few successful and viable commercial operations using artificially heated water.

9. Can any pollutants enter the culture ponds? Careful checks should be made upsteam, if river water is being used, as to whether or not there are, or will be in the future, any factories discharging effluents into the river. The local farming community should, in addition, be watched as they may seasonally discharge crop protection chemical sprays or cattle dips into the river with disastrous effects. Borehole water should be, to a large extent, free from pollutants. It is unusual at the moment to recycle water through eel culture ponds, though

in the future, as technical know-how advances, water purification units may be used to remove waste products and to prevent the build-up of undesirable chemicals so that water can be recycled several times.

10. Is the water quality satisfactory? The ideal pH of the available water should be slightly alkaline with a value of between 7 and 8. Acidic waters limit eel growth the effects of which can be reduced within reason by liming. The iron content of the water should be checked to ensure the concentration of one element does not make other elements unavailable to eels.

11. Can predators be easily eliminated? The number and incidence of predators feeding on cultured eels in the ponds is low. The elver rearing stage is most susceptible to attacks, though as they are increasingly housed indoors, these are kept to a minimum. Few precautions, such as putting up wires, are taken. Normally, during the day, there is always someone patrolling the ponds which tends to scare away any would-be attackers.

12. Can the site be protected from poachers? Regrettably, this is an increasingly important point as many fish culture farms in a competitive business are so vulnerable to poaching, or to the intentional vindictive introduction of chemicals to the water. Many years of hard work can so easily be destroyed in the space of a few unguarded minutes. It is easy to be wise after the event. More and more farms have fences round the perimeter and a regular patrol and guard are maintained.

There are, in addition to the questions relating to the physical and environmental features of a potential eel culture farm, many others which need either to be satisfactorily answered or which the would-be investor should be aware of at the outset. These include those relating to the biological aspects of the eel; feed and equipment availability; and marketing and management objectives. Outside the Far East some of these questions do not as yet have answers and they represent a considerable risk factor to potential investors in eel culture.

1. How much literature is available on eel culture? This book gives a comprehensive coverage of the limited amount of literature published to date. Further worthwhile data can be

obtained by referring to the books and authors listed at the back.

2. What is known of the growth rate of eels? Eels take approximately 18–24 months to reach a market size of 200 gms in the Far East. Can this or a better figure be achieved in the area and with the culture system planned?

3. How much production per unit area can be expected? An average production level of 2 kg of eels per square metre of water surface per annum is a good figure to start with, provided disease incidence is kept to a minimum. However, this has not been achieved outside the Far East.

4. Have all eel diseases known now been identified? No, they have not. There are still a number of diseases in the Far East with unidentified causes and for which no effective control is yet available. It does not necessarily follow that the same diseases attacking eels in the Far East will also occur elsewhere. There could well be another disease spectrum. Other disease questions include: Are suitable facilities available for detecting diseases as soon as they appear? What laboratory facilities and zoologists are available locally to assist in the quick identification of diseases and to suggest proper control techniques? What costs may be involved?

5. What feeds are available for eels? Few manufacturers outside the Far East have researched and developed feeds for eels although several of the more prominent compounders claim they would be able to quickly produce a suitable ration, should a demand arise. Many are very willing, meantime, to provide experimental feeds.

6. What supporting equipment is available for eel culture? The same answer applies as for feeds above and considerable improvisation will be necessary to begin with though, of course, items such as grinders, mixers, water pumps are readily available.

7. In what form and when will the eels be processed, packed and marketed? What facilities are needed for handling, processing and marketing eels? A guide to the possible answers to these questions is provided in this book.

8. Some of the questions which should be asked with regard to management include: Can you hire suitable personnel at a reasonable salary to carry out all phases of the operation?

What safeguards can be built into the operation against emergencies? Is it possible, if necessary, to switch from eel culture into other forms of culture? Can routine checks be made on chemical aspects of the water? Will conservation laws restrict the farming operations? What biological and business records need to be maintained? Is additional land available for enlarging operations should expansion seem feasible?

Eel Farm Capital Requirements and Returns

The capital requirements of an eel culture farm outlined in this section are sub-divided into fixed and variable costs. In economic terms, in the long run there are no such costs as fixed costs. However, in spite of the limitations of the use of this term, the main costs involved in establishing the farm, structural and equipment facilities are defined as fixed costs, or in other words as expenditure which does not vary in the short term. Variable costs, in contrast, cover day to day expenditure and vary directly with the rate of output and efficiency.

Fixed Costs

The main fixed cost capital expenditure items are clearly outlined in Table 24. These costs are based on data obtained in a survey of 30 eel producers in Taiwan, the results of which were published in November 1973. There is a slight difference in cost between establishing a culture pond for Japanese eels as opposed to European eels. The latter require a pond which is 135 cm (5 ft) deep, instead of 108 cm (4 ft). The other costs are the same.

In the costings, the ponds are built with concrete walls, and their average size is 0.1–0.2 hectare. The electrical equipment includes a generator, cooling machine, electric wiring and lighting. The provision of an office, workshop and store makes up the building costs. The charge for well and water pumps estimate an average of 1.5 wells being sunk and 10–15 hp being provided per hectare. Each pond has 1–2 sets of paddle wheels and the surrounding guardfence has concrete columns with wire netting in between.

All fixed costs given in Table 24 are approximate costs per hectare for establishing an eel farm smaller than three hectares. The average fixed cost per hectare for such items as pond construction, wells, paddle wheels vary little, whereas the average costs per hectare of the remaining items reduce as the farm size increases.

Table 24 – Fixed costs per hectare ($£$)

Item	Cost $£$
Pond construction	5,000
Electrical equipment	1,600
Buildings	1,000
Borehole wells	550
Water pumps	330
Paddle wheel and electric motor	360
Guard surrounding fences	450
Nets	100
Truck and motor cycle	400
Miscellaneous	210
TOTAL FIXED COSTS	$£$10,000

This is a convenient and easy figure to remember. In contrast to a farm of under 3 hectares, the average fixed costs per hectare for a farm of over five hectares are $£$8,500. Neither of these figures, include the purchase price of the land or any allowance for depreciation or interest charges.

Variable Costs
The two main variable cost items are feed and the purchase price of elvers. Skilful buying in either case can lead to a considerable reduction in costs. The price of elvers varies enormously with Japanese eel elvers, as already outlined, being particularly expensive. In the costings for a farm of under three hectares the stocking density per hectare is assumed to be 12 eels per sq m^2, or 120,000 individuals, with each Japanese elver costing 5p or $£$330/kg to buy in. This figure is below the average price of $£$460 per kilo paid by farmers in 1973.

A compound feed charge of 8.5p is allocated to each eel based on – a survival rate of 50 per cent; a conversion rate of 2.3:1; and a feed price of 20p/kg. Wages are calculated on the basis of 2.20 regular, and 0·64 temporary workers being required per hectare. The wage rate is $£$35 per month for male workers, and about $£$25 for female workers. These figures, of course, will need considerable modification before application to other parts of the world. Maintenance and repair, electricity, and chemical costs need no further explanation. A charge for land rental is included in the Taiwan study as a variable cost as opposed to land purchase appearing as a fixed cost.

Table 25 – Variable costs per hectare per annum (£)

Item/cost	(£)
Elvers @ 5p each	6,000
Feed @ 8.5p each	5,100
Wages	1,300
Maintenance and repairs	1,150
Electricity	400
Chemicals	270
Rent	270
Miscellaneous	500
TOTAL VARIABLE COSTS	£14,990

The purchase of elvers and feed accounts for over 75 per cent of the variable costs. The advantages of economy in this direction can be clearly seen. If, instead, a charge of 7.5p is allocated to each elver bought (bringing the cost per kilo up to £450) and an increased charge of 10·5p per eel for feed is made on a 70 per cent survival rate, then the total variable costs are raised to £21,710 per hectare.

Fortunately, for the Japanese and Taiwanese eel farmers, they are not solely dependent on having to culture their own species of eel, and are able to buy in European elvers at a much reduced price. In the new calculations, the average buying in price to the farmer is 1p per elver, or £36 per kilo, as there are 3,600 European elvers to a kilo, as opposed to 6,000 Japanese elvers to a kilo. The same stocking density of 120,000 per hectare is assumed, though there is a tendency to further increase the density when elvers are cheaper. A feed cost of 8.5p and a harvesting rate of 10 per cent produces total variable costs of £6,110 per hectare. Feed and elver costs no longer account for 75 per cent of the variable costs and are now in the region of 40 per cent. Similarly, if each European elver costs 2p each to buy or £72 per kilo (which is extremely high for 1973) and 10.5p to fatten with a 70 per cent harvesting rate, then the total variable cost per hectare is £15,110. No charges are included in any of the variable cost figures for marketing live eels. These would be large if live eels are airfreighted to Tokyo.

The average variable cost per hectare for such items as wages, maintenance and repairs, electricity and chemicals are reduced slightly as the farm size increases from below three hectares to about five hectares, whereas the average ground rent charge per hectare is constant.

Revenue

The most important consideration to be made once fixed and variable costs have been established is to calculate the annual returns per hectare, so as to estimate whether or not a reasonable return on capital invested can be made. High and low average variable costs per hectare have been outlined above for both Japanese and European eel production. The same cost figures are used in Table 26 from which potential returns are deduced.

The main factors affecting survival and harvesting rates are – the incidence of disease; stocking density; water temperature; water quality and food supply. At the present time, the European eel does not compare favourably in terms of survival rates with the

Table **26** – Annual revenue per hectare (£)

Japanese eel (elver/feed cost (p))	Production of eel (Kg/ha)	Annual Revenue (£)	Variable costs (£)
50% harvested (5/8.5)	10,000	20,000	14,990
70% harvested (7.5/10.5)	14,000	28,000	21,710
European eel			
10% harvested (1/8.5)	2,000	4,000	6,110
70% harvested (2/10.5)	14,000	28,000	15,110

Japanese eel. The average price received by farmers in 1973 per kilo is taken as £2, with no price variation between Japanese and European eels. The average time taken to fatten Japenese eels to a market size of 5–6 pieces per kilo is 12 months, whereas European eels take an average of 14 months.

The estimated gross margins per hectare are £5,010; £6,290; £2,110; and £12,890 respectively. Management objectives are, of course, to buy in elvers as cheaply as possible and to achieve a high survival rate. These returns must be offset against the depreciation rate of fixed costs decided upon before arriving at a final profit and a percentage return on capital. No marketing charges are included in these figures, neither are any charges made for salaried management.

It is easy to permutate figures on paper to produce startling profit results. The real test is, of course, what is achieved in practice as there are many financial risks involved in eel culture. In conclusion, it is estimated an average European eel harvesting rate of 25 per cent, compared with a Japanese rate of 70 per cent, is necessary for a culture farm to break-even.

The Potential for Eel Culture in Europe

A distinction has been made between extensive and intensive culture at the outset of this section. Extensive eel culture has been widely practised in Europe for a number of years of which the operations of the Dutch, Germans and Northern Irish are best known in this field. Annually, large numbers of elvers are transported from their capture point along the European coastline to inland lakes or water areas. Here the outlets are restricted with control barriers to ensure those elvers or eels released in these areas remain there and do not migrate to other waters.

The growth rate of extensively cultured eels is, of course, the same as those in the wild. The whole operation depends on the natural environment and the prevailing climatic conditions and there is little the extensive culture farmer or fisherman can do to speed up the production rate. The eels reach an acceptable market size of 150–200 gms in 5–6 years, and are caught as either brown or silver eels. Extensive culture is attractive in that overheads are low and, generally, waters which would not otherwise be utilised do yield a return. More and more people with access to suitable waters are showing an interest in culturing eels as the market price for eel flesh increases. There are many ponds, lakes and dykes which could be rewardingly stocked with elvers both within and outside the countries already practising extensive eel culture in Europe.

Water temperature is the main factor which limits intensive eel culture. The European eel despite the environment it lives in thrives in a warm water temperature in the region of 23–25 °C in order to sustain its maximum growth rate. In the natural environment this level is rarely reached for more than 2–3 months of the year and the growing season is probably limited to only 6–7 months. Intensive eel culture to date has, therefore, been limited to either scientific aquatic work, or to one or two pilot schemes in Southern Europe. The latitude in the South of France is 43°50′, which compares unfavourably with that of the eel culture region of Taiwan of 22–25°.

The bank of information on eel diseases, feed and other topics under European conditions is limited as the whole concept is still in its infancy. The Japanese and Taiwanese are very much the leaders in this field. Throughout Europe, however, there is a fast growing awareness of the need to develop fish culture and an increasing concentration of technical and financial resources are being invested. Eels with a ready home market will certainly be one of the fish species to be considered. There is a growing amount of talk about the application of controlled environments to the culture industry. This is essential because fish are so susceptible to disease and temperature changes. No doubt, in a relatively short period scientists will find a way to heat and maintain the pond water temperature economically at 25 °C throughout the year, and one of the main obstacles limiting intensive eel culture adoption in Europe at the moment will then be removed.

Section 3–Eel Capture

INTRODUCTION

An understanding of eel behaviour patterns, like those of any other fish it is intended to capture, is essential if the right methods of capture are to be adopted. The eel is caught in two stages of development. Firstly, as a brown or yellow eel, when it is feeding and developing in a river or estuary (the term brown eel is used throughout this section though some would hold that the term yellow eel is more appropriate); secondly, as a larger sized and older silver eel, which has completed its feeding, and is in the process of beginning the long migration back to the spawning ground. The behaviour pattern of these two types of eel is different, and that affects the kind of fishing gear an eel fisherman uses. The first section outlines some of the behaviour and migration patterns of brown and silver European eels, and discusses some of the factors influencing their movements.

EEL BEHAVIOUR PATTERNS
Brown eels

Brown eels are nocturnal in habit and feed on the river bed mostly during the night. They eat crustacea and the spawn of coarse fishes. By day they hide away from strong sunlight in the mud or under stones on the bottom, or in masses of plants. Smaller eels are, however, less inhibited by light than larger ones, and thus are more inclined to continue their upstream movement in daylight. Such a migration may occur in huge numbers with fingerling eels measuring between 17–22 cm, and this movement is commercially exploited for restocking purposes in Holland and Germany.

The definition of at what size or weight brown eels can be taken from the water varies according to the legislation of different countries. In Holland, the minimum permitted size is 28 cm, whereas in Northern Ireland, the minimum weight brown eel which can be taken is 5 oz. Any eel size or weight under these limits must be returned to the water to grow on.

Larger brown eels show less temperature sensitivity than the smaller eels, but in general the activity of eels is decreased by low water temperatures. Below a water temperature of 5 °C eels become inactive, and at temperatures of less than 9°C food bait is ignored. Temperature regulates the beginning and end of the brown eel fishing season, which normally starts in Europe in April or May, and continues through until September. At this time eel fishermen switch their interest towards the more valuable silver eels. In practice brown eel capture involves cheap and fairly simple gear. Brown eels are more likely to be attracted to baited eels traps early in the season, rather than later, when there are usually more than adequate supplies of natural feed available in the water. During the winter months brown eels, for the greater part, lie motionless in mud.

Throughout the summer months brown eels feed in the river, and this may involve a certain amount of migration from one feeding ground to another depending on supplies. Not all eels, however, migrate in the summer; some stay put. Summer up-stream migratory movements take place against a flow of water. In still water, migration in the summer usually only begins when a considerable amount of water flows into the still-water area. Moving further up-stream, as one would expect, eels show an increase in size. This may be due either to the presence of older eels or better feeding grounds being found upstream, or to a higher proportion of larger females in the population. Larger numbers of male than female eels are found in saline river estuaries, and vice versa for the inland freshwater.

Migration begins at the beginning of April, and goes on until late autumn. Movement starts at a water temperature of 8–9°C, and increases in intensity as the water temperature rises. Migration is distinctly more active during the night, than in daylight. A considerable proportion of a local brown eel population may be on the move during some period of the summer. As the season progresses the length of the period of activity builds up as the night lengthens. During the night maximum swimming activity occurs after dusk, and is lowest before dawn. Maximum activity also usually coincides with a waning moon, and especially with a new moon; and as one would expect normally less activity takes place during a full moon. Brown eel migration is not solely related to finding feeding grounds – it also involves migration to hibernation grounds.

The brown eel has most efficient and sensitive smell organs, which make up for poor vision. Their eyes are small at this stage. Eels are only attracted by fresh natural bait. Some chemicals used for the preservation of netting or to fix knots, may even repulse eels when they approach contact. While in their refuges eels can be very resistant to strong and unpleasant odours; and can stay in water contaminated to such an extent that their meat even becomes unpalatable. When baiting lines, fishermen should take care their hands are clean, as such things as oil or kerosene on the hands can cause a sharp decrease in the catch.

It has been observed that eels leave the water to forage and feed on such things as slugs and worms on land. On hot summer days eels are lazy feeders and can be taken on a long line by using special sized baits such as ruff or small perch. Pike, cormorants, and otters are predators of eels. Eels enter voluntarily into traps which simulate a shelter. Their motivation to enter them is not only due to an urge to move away from light, but also to a strong reaction to touch; they like the whole body to come into contact with a solid surface. Eels are most restless during thunderstorms.

Silver eels
Silver eels, are so called because of the coloration of their bellies, and this is a sign they have reached sexual maturity, and are now ready to begin their migration to sea perhaps after having fed in a river for seven or more years. Other signs of an eel preparing to migrate are the development of very large eyes and the acquisition of elongated pointed pectoral fins which will enable an eel to swim for long interrupted stretches. All these changes adapt a European eel for its 3,600 miles long sea trip.

The body fat content of a European silver eel may be as high as 28%, which contrasts with a brown eel fat content of about 11%. A mature eel has a calorific value in the region of 1,350 calories per lb which compares very favourably with other forms of animal protein. Silver eels are therefore in the peak of condition when weighing up to 2 kg each, and are then most valuable. Their capture often requires large, robust, and fairly expensive equipment, and in many fast flowing rivers it is difficult and even impossible.

Silver eels are best caught as they migrate downstream, as opposed to when they are feeding, which by this stage has ceased, so therefore different types of fishing gear are used to those needed for brown eels. Peak migrations occur towards the end of the year in October and November, though for a number of reasons it may be extended over other months. Freezing cold spells of weather in the winter interrupt migrations, which may not be resumed again until well into the next year. The number of eels migrating in the autumn also varies between male and female eels. Relatively more females migrate at the end of the season than at the beginning, and the bigger males are the first to migrate at the beginning of the season.

The migration of silver eels in freshwater occurs almost entirely between sunset and midnight and the largest concentration moving just after sunset. Silver eel migration should not be pictured as occuring daily throughout these months, but on only two or three nights in large quantities when all the different conditions are favourable.

There are a number of factors influencing the intensity of movement of European silver eels. These include, depth of water; the phase of the moon; the strength and level of water flow; the coloration of the water; prevailing weather conditions; and the presence of inflowing seawater into a river.

Water depth appears to have an important influence on when eels migrate. Deep water areas hold migrating eels for one or two months longer than shallow water areas, which are associated with early summer migrations. This variation may have something to do with the fact that eels have on a number of occasions been known to mass in large numbers before departing.

The influence of the moon on the movement of silver eels is well known. The best catches are made in the periods between the last and first quarter of the moon, when the nights are darkest. The last quarter is also that part of the lunar month during which moonlight falls early in the night, which ties in well with the main migration occurring shortly after sunset.

Increases in the water flow rate, and rises in the water level, are associated with an increase in the number of migrating eels. Eels under these conditions are able to migrate with a minimum of swimming effort, thus conserving energy for the much longer haul against the ocean currents back to the spawning ground. The water level in a river may have dropped to such an extent in the summer months, that the flow is restricted, and eels are isolated in river pools.

Silver eels are only released from these pools when heavy rains increase the water flow. Heavy rains are of course associated with an increased run off of water from the land carrying with it erosion products, which discolour the water. Often eel migrations coincide with dirty coloured water.

On a highly technical plane, the number of silver eels migrating has been correlated to microseisms, that is the frequency with which the ground vibrates, normally in response to depressions at sea. The frequency can be measured, and it has been established that the number of eels migrating increases sharply only after the occurrence of microseisms as frequent as one every three seconds, or in other words when storm conditions are developing, and there is a low depression over the North Sea and the English Channel. A number of eel fishermen keep a few silver eels they have previously caught in a holding tank, and when these eels become restless they know this is a sign there is going to be a change in the weather, and a storm is brewing. They then imply eels will be running in the river, and it should be a good night for catching them.

Silver eel movement from freshwater may be stimulated by salt water. Using this information, in Northern Italy, salt water is introduced into the valli to induce an increased migration of silver eels.

Silver eels migrating in inland waters, where there are no distractions, swim with the current if there is one, expending very little energy. The force of river flow determines whereabouts in a river an eel moves in its migration. Sometimes in fast flowing conditions they may be found in large numbers on the opposite bank to that used under slow flow conditions. Generally, an eel swims in or is guided to, the area of greatest flow, and this will normally be where the river is deepest. It is at this point that catching barriers are placed.

Wind direction can increase silver eel catches. Numbers caught may be especially high if the direction of a strong wind coincides with that of the river flow. There is no one wind direction which is more favourable than another. In Northern Ireland on Lough Neagh, a strong southerly wind increases catches in the River Bann. On Windermere, a northerly wind has the same effect.

It is thought the use of a strong artificial light could change the migration direction of eels, and make it possible for nets to be positioned in the area to which they are deflected. However, artificial lights are not used commercially to direct eels, though by contrast, they may be turned on to stop a migration, or to reduce its intensity.

The influence of electricity on eels is well known, and is described in the section on catching brown eels. It is dubious whether its influence can be used commercially to change the migration route of silver eels. Experiments carried out in Southern Ireland indicate total catches without the use of electricity are much higher, and only half the eels allow themselves to be directed towards the anode.

Very few migrating silver eels are caught at sea as opposed to brackish water. This may be because either the eels swim at low depths, or there are no strong influences to concentrate them into one area, and so they migrate over a wide area. A few eels have been successfully caught in shallow brackish water by using nets towed behind a fast moving boat. But eel fishermen usually have to rely on fixed nets or installations to catch silver eels. In some cases, fyke nets can be strategically placed, where a migration may strike a difficult place, and be forced to follow the coastline for some distance.

A number of experiments using tags have been carried out to measure the rate at which an eel can swim. The maximum distance covered in a day may be as far as 60 km, which is a considerable distance, if an eel travels only at night. An average rate of progress is 20–25 km a day.

There are indications silver eels migrate in the sea in the upper water layers. However, little conclusive information is available about the route silver eels follow, and their behaviour pattern, once they have left fresh and brackish water, and have begun the long trip back to the spawning ground.

METHODS USED TO CATCH BROWN EELS

All the fishing methods used to catch brown eels depend to a greater or lesser extent on the feeding and migratory behaviour of brown eels. Either baited or unbaited fishing traps can be set for their capture. The following more important methods of brown eel capture are outlined: clotting, spears, eel combs, long lines, baited traps, baited eel boxes, electrofishing, seine and fyke nets.

Clotting

Clotting is a method of catching eels which has been traditionally practised in many parts of Great Britain for a number of years.

This method is not used commercially, since only a limited number of eels can be caught at any one time. The clotting stick is a 200–250 cm long pole at the end of which is attached at right angles a length of firm wire. Fresh worms are threaded onto a piece of wool 100–120 cm long, bundled up, and tied to the wire on the end of the stick. As an alternative bait, the guts of a rabbit or poultry are used providing they are fresh.

The pole is held in fast running water. Brown eels swim in to grab the worms, and as they do so, the stick is quickly lifted out of the water, with the eel still holding on to the worms and wool. An eel weighing up to 500–600 g can be caught using this method, though the size of eel taken is limited by the breaking strain of the wool. Clotting is more effective early in the season in May and June, when there is only a limited amount of natural feed in the river. Worms offered at this time are particularly tempting. The best weather condition for clotting is a heavy spring thunderstorm.

Spears

Eel spears are one of the oldest types of fishing gear used to catch brown eels. They can have one or more prongs, which may be barbed. The distance between the prongs can be regulated by law according to the country where the spears are used. All spears have long wooden handles, the length of which is limited by buoyancy which increases with length. A length of 7 m is considered to be the practical limit.

Eels are spotted blowing bubbles to the water surface as they lie resting in the mud during the daytime, or at night with the aid of an artificial light. With a quick movement the fisherman impales the eel with his spear, but as quite often happens he may miss and the eel escapes badly injured. For this reason the use of spears is forbidden in some countries. Special barriers can be constructed to increase yields by forcing eels through a restricted area, from where they are speared. The flesh of a speared eel is always damaged, and they must therefore be sold as quickly as possible before their condition deteriorates too much.

There are a number of different types of spears. For example, Danish eel fishermen use spears on which the prongs have been replaced by spring clamps. These catch and hold the eel without wounding it, and are therefore considered to be the best kind of spear. Sometimes spears with both clamps and prongs are used.

Eel Combs

Eel combs have been used in Europe and Asia, for many years although their use is now prohibited in most countries, because similarly to spears, the eel can often escape though badly wounded. The comb is usually towed through mud, and pierces any eel which happens to be lying in its path; a barbaric way of catching eels.

Long Lines

Long lines are widely used throughout Europe to catch brown eels. Each long line consists of a main line to which is attached at equal distances a variable number of branch lines carrying baited hooks which normally lie on the river or estuary base. There are many different ways of constructing a long line, with variations in the length of branch lines, the distance between branch lines, and the size and shape of the hooks. The distance between branch lines varies from 1.8–4.5 m, and the length of branch lines from 0.3–1.8 m. Branch lines should never be longer than half the spacing between them. In this way, the entangling of hooks with each other will be avoided. The number of hooks or branches per long line varies from 40 to several hundred, but there are usually between 100–250 per line. Sometimes a number of long lines are joined together to form a line with perhaps as many as 1000 hooks on it.

Most lines are now made of nylon, as this has been found to be more efficient than other types of material. The thinner the line the better, as this is less discernible to the eel. The material used for the branch line is generally weaker than that of the main line, so that under heavy stress it snaps first. The choice of the right shape and size hook is very important. A small hook can be swallowed too deeply by an eel, becoming impossible to remove, whereas a large hook cannot be taken by a small eel. The recommended hooks are, the 'Kirby' hook, with a point bent sideways, of sizes No. 2/0 to No. 2, and the 'Carlisle' hook, with a straight point, of sizes No. 18/10 mm and No. 18/7 mm.

Many different types of bait are used on long lines. These include: dew worms (which are particularly popular in Canada); whole small live fish; and pieces of any fresh fish which can be easily and regularly obtained such as smelt, gudgeon, roach, perch and herring. If a fisherman is using small live fish for bait, which he has caught with a seine net, then the hooks are baited as the line is set. Care is taken not to wound the fish too much when baiting up, so that it remains alive to attract eels for a longer period of time.

Two men are necessary for long line setting from a boat. One baits the hooks and throws out the line, while the other keeps the boat on the right course at the right speed. Sometimes the layout of the line may be zigzagged from shallow to deeper waters with a weight placed at each angle. The line is normally loosely set on the ground, because otherwise the eel taking the baited hook would quickly feel the resistance in the line, and let go. The beginning and end of a long line are marked by anchored buoys, or the line may be connected to a stake on a river bank. The line need not always be set on the ground. Sometimes in Canada, lines are set with good results in freshwater deeper than 5 m and deliberately suspended off the bottom by attaching floats.

Lines are usually set late in the afternoon or in the evening, and lifted early the next morning, before hooked eels become too active, and have a chance to escape. Captured eels are cut from the branch line, and put into a water tank or net bag to keep them alive on board boat. Some eels' mouths and insides may be badly damaged when the hooks are taken out, so long lined eels are sold quickly before their condition deteriorates. This method of fishing does not discriminate between different sizes of eel, both small and under-sized eels are caught as well as larger eels.

Eels can be caught on long lines positioned over sand or gravel bottoms, but the best catches are made on a mud bottom with or without rocks, or in other words, in any river or estuary where the hooks do not entangle with weeds. Long lines can be trawled some-times. Highest catches are made on dark nights after a new moon, especially when following rain or a storm, and in warm weather. The long line season lasts from May until late autumn, with the best catches being taken early in the season.

Night lines are a variation of long line fishing. A length of line is baited with a chunk of eel, or a small bird from a nest, and thrown into a deep water hole in a river, left over night, and lifted early the next morning. A number of single lines are set in any one pool.

Baited Eel Box
Baited eel boxes are widely used by eel fishermen on Ijsselmeer, in Holland instead of long lines. A narrow open ended box measuring

70 × 11 × 11 cm, is made out of 1 cm thick wooden battens nailed together. The opening at each end is fitted with a simple nylon mesh funnel shaped inlet, which offers little or no resistance to eels entering, but prevents their escape. The nylon funnel inlets on either end are kept open by a piece of string connecting them. The top of the box is fitted with a sliding lid, which is removed to put bait in, and to take eels out. The bottom of the box is weighted by two iron bars, which ensure the box sinks and remains in a horizontal position.

Rather like branch lines on a long line, boxes are attached at regular intervals of 25 m to a 750 m long main line, by 1 m long cords. Similarly, the end of a line is marked by a buoy, or is secured to a river bank. Generally, though, their use is limited to still-waters. A crew of three may set and lift up to 300 boxes, which can be neatly stacked on board the boat. They are easy to handle and set. Before a box is placed in the water, a handful of bait such as fish roes, worms, or old cheese, or in fact anything releasing a good attracting odour, is put into each, and the lid replaced. The boxes are set at dusk, and lifted the next day at dawn.

The box resembles a dark tube, and if sufficient smell is exuded by the bait, then feeding eels are attracted in to it. Some fishermen, in order to improve the fishing efficiency, make two additional openings on the sides of the box, making four entrances in total. A new box is not usually placed immediately in case it carries a repellant smell from the wood used. Before use, boxes are kept immersed for several weeks to absorb the specific smell of the water. Some fishermen, to make the attracting smell even more realistic, keep live eels in them for a short while.

Baited eel boxes were first used on any scale in Holland in 1966, when just under five tons of eels were taken; by 1970 this figure reached a peak of over 500 tons, which has now dropped to an annual average in the region of 200 tons. Unlike long lines, baited eel boxes cause no damage to eels, and ensure their marketability.

Baited Traps

Baited eel traps, perhaps the best known method of catching eels, are made from a variety of materials depending on what is available locally, and in almost every shape and size. Irrespective of what they are made of, all traps operate on the same basic principle, that is, to attract feeding brown eels into their area. Influenced by the scent, an eel locates where the bait is, and swims towards it into a rapidly narrowing funnel entrance, which opens into an inner chamber from where there is little or no chance of escape. The bait is either placed free in the trap or crushed up and put into a sock or bag from which odours slowly diffuse. This prevents the bait from being eaten up by any eels already caught.

The stronger the smell, the quicker an inquisitive eel is attracted. The bait used varies depending on what is available locally and how much it costs. Earth worms make a good bait in fresh water, and herring are successful in estuaries. Offal of slaughtered cattle or other livestock give off a particularly strong odour, which is attractive providing the flesh is not too old and rotten. As a rule, the fresher the bait, the better the chance of catching eels. The bait offered therefore varies according to whether it is to be fished in fresh or salt water. A fisherman usually tries to match the bait with the feed which normally makes up an eel's diet in its natural environment.

Traps are set daily at dusk, when old bait is removed, and replaced by fresh bait. The best time to catch brown eels is in the first two hours of darkness, and some fishermen may return later the same night to lift their traps, rather than wait until early the next morning. Eels can be caught in traps during the day, if the weather is dull and overcast, or the water is muddy. The best conditions however are dark and stormy nights.

Fishing with baited traps, as with any other baited eel fishing, begins in April in Europe, and continues until late autumn. The best catches are recorded early in the summer, as the water temperature and eels' activity increases, and vice versa catches dwindle in the autumn as the water temperature and eels' activity declines.

Traps are set singly or together in any convenient section of a river, lake or estuary. The bottom of a trap is heavily weighted either with cement, iron bars, or some other material to keep it in position when it is used in fast flowing waters. The trap is placed with its mouth facing downstream when used in a river, and in estuaries it is directed towards the incoming tide. Here traps are set at low tide; the fishermen positioning them in the narrow channels running between the mud flats. Marker buoys identify where the traps have been set.

One of the best ways to classify the different types of baited eel traps available is on the basis of the materials used in their construction. These may include, wire, wood, willow cane, or just a simple farm sack. The shape and size specifications within these types of material vary enormously, and the figures given below serve only as a guideline, and should be adjusted to suit the environment in which a baited trap is to be fished.

An effective wire eel trap is made by stretching 1 cm mesh, heavy gauge galvanised wire netting over a rectangular framework of stout fencing wire measuring 100 × 40 × 30 cm. One or more tapering funnels of wire netting project about 25 cm into the cage, and a hatch is built on the top of the trap for baiting and removing eels. The underside is normally weighted to keep the trap in position. Alternatively, a wire eel trap can be cylindrical in shape, measuring 100 to 160 cm in length, from 20 to 40 cm in diameter, and covered with 1 cm wire netting. The funnel core is made of 1.5 cm mesh with the small inner end having a 10 cm opening reinforced by a metal ring. An additional central funnel can be built which is the same as the first funnel described, except that the smaller aperture is only 5 cm in diameter. Eels swim through one or both of these funnels into a compartment which has an end opening made of cotton netting tied up by a purse string. The trap is stabilised by flat iron bars on either side of the cylinder to which ballasting, or a marker buoy are attached. At the beginning of each season, the trap is tarred to increase its longevity.

Wooden eel traps follow much the same design as lobster pots, with a gap of 6–10 mm between each wooden lathe making up the trap. At one or both ends cone-shaped nylon or 1 cm wire mesh netting leads the eels into a holding chamber. These traps are simple, light and easy to handle.

Basket baited eel traps are used in England, though they frequently fill up rapidly with waste material. They are made out of willow branches woven together to form a cone-shaped structure, with a funnel leading into the main trap chamber. The end of the cone is covered with nylon netting from which captured eels are removed. This type of trap, closely resembles the eels' natural environment by providing it with a concealed, darkened refuge. They are now expensive and time consuming to make, and should be soaked before use.

A simple effective Heath Robinson type trap can be made from filling a sack up with straw, and placing an old drain pipe into it. Eels enter along the pipe, feed, and then lie up in the straw.

Baited eel traps are either single, double, or multi-entry, as exemplified by the baited eel box used in Holland. In this way the potential fishing efficiency is increased as eels may be fished for in two or more directions simultaneously. No figures can be given for the exact cost of constructing baited eel traps, though they are unlikely to be more than £5 each.

Electrofishing

In theory, electrofishing promises the most efficient method of catching eels. In practise however, it is not used widely commercially, partly because of the relatively low returns recorded for the amount of fishing effort put in, and the variable temperament of the equipment used. More time may be taken up getting the gear to work satisfactorily than is actually spent fishing. Electrofishing is, though, invaluable when removing eels from relatively inaccessible areas, such as from the mud left behind after a pond has been drained, where obviously nets would be ineffective, or from waters where there are many obstructions and weeds. The method is well suited for use in streams with a depth not greater than 180 cm.

The following notes outline a few basic principles involved with electrofishing. For a more comprehensive understanding readers are advised to refer to *Fishing with Electricity*, a book prepared as a result of a symposium held by FAO for European authorities on this subject.

The eel is very responsive to alternating and direct current electrical stimuli. In a direct current field, eels turn to face the positive electrode, and swim towards it, and remain as close as possible to it until they are removed. In this way, under the influence of the electrical field, eels emerge from under stones and gravel, and swim vigorously towards the positive electrode. Electrified eels are easy to catch partly because they are stunned, and partly because they are clearly visible. Generally speaking, there is no loss of consciousness, but if the electrical field is sufficiently strong they may turn over. In this condition their bodies are entirely relaxed, and they recover instantly when the current is switched off.

The anode or the positive electrode may be made either of wire netting placed on a frame, or of expanded metal, mounted on a well waxed wooden handle. The blade may be scoop shaped or in the form of a wire basket. Eels swim into the positive electrode basket and are easily captured. A possible disadvantage of this system is that any other eels in the vicinity, which have not entered the scoop, instantly escape at full speed when the field is interrupted. It is therefore as well to have two or more anodes working together, which are lifted alternatively so as to keep the field intact. Another solution is to keep the anode in the water and remove the eels with hand nets from alongside it. In this case the anode should, of course, be flat, to avoid obstructing the net.

The cathode in direct current fishing may be thought of as an earth return. There is no particular advantage having it positioned near the positive electrode, and it may therefore be left in a more convenient location near the generator, while the positive electrodes are used. Its function is to connect the negative side of the system to the river or stream bed and this is done either by a sheet of expanded metal, or a mat of wire netting, or where movement is necessary, by a trailing chain. The only essential is that it should be large enough to pass all the current required. It is advantageous to have the negative electrode in the deepest water convenient, particularly where the river bottom is rocky or gravelled. Mud is a good conductor, and increases the effective size of a cathode laid in it. It is nearly always best to work up-stream, as this avoids mud stirred up from wading.

Effective DC fishing requires a voltage of about 250 at the electrodes, maintained by a generator. The optimum AC impulse frequency for eels is 30–50 Hz. In practice, the generator unit may be placed beside the stream, where it is convenient to lower the negative electrode into a hole, and the positive electrode or electrodes are connected to a control panel by cables up to 50 m long. These are carried and played out as the eel fisherman advances using the electrodes to probe into likely lies or eddies on the bottom of a stream, or to explore beds of weeds. Various drums have been designed to allow the cable to be carried on the fisherman's back, but in practice it is perfectly simple to hold a 50 m coil of cable in one hand. The ability to drop everything with safety in case of a fall is most valuable.

There are variations in the behaviour of electro fishing equipment when different water conditions are encountered. Conductivity is increased both by a rise in temperature, and by an increase in dissolved salts. The current demand is considerable, and the behaviour of sets may vary considerably, both from point to point, and from day to day. Best yields are obtained at night, and in low water levels. The most effective time to electrofish in Europe, is between late autumn and early spring, when eels are hibernating in the mud, and when other capture methods are relatively ineffective. An important drawback to electrofishing is that it is unselective. It attracts all kinds of other fish, and for this reason in many instances its use is limited. The anode instead of being fitted to a scoop net, may be incorporated into a seine net.

An eel becomes cramped when an alternating current, instead of a direct current is used. Its muscles contract, the gills expand and the eel rapidly becomes inert. When the current is switched off, the eel revives after an interval depending on the duration and severity of the shock it has received. In running waters eels are immobilised between the poles for a brief period before being swept away out of the electrical field. As a rule there are no after effects, but in some cases damage to the backbone can result from excessive stresses. The essential requirement is that passive eels should be collected before they revive. No reliance can be placed on removing all the eels from a stretch of water, as this method only turns and stops the eels in the vicinity of the electrodes.

Seine Nets

Seine nets trawled behind a powered boat can be used to catch eels in smooth bottomed, slow moving waters. A net up to 100 m long, and 100–150 cm deep at the centre is manageable. The wings can be of about 7–8 cm mesh, and the long poke or bag of 6 mm mesh. The net has to be operated quickly using a heavily weighted ground rope to maintain close contact with the bottom of a river or estuary. The handling of heavy seine nets of large dimensions need a great amount of manpower, and for this reason their use has declined, while other catching methods have improved.

Alternatively, seine nets may be electrified by using a direct current field. One problem encountered using such seine nets is that the encircled eels escape in large numbers during the last phase of fishing, when the net is being drawn in. The upper and lower lines are electrified, and the width of the mouth of the net can be as large as 25 m. Electrified seine nets, of course, have the disadvantage that they catch a lot of other species of fish at the same time as eels, and this restricts their use.

Fyke Nets

Fyke nets are used for catching both brown and silver eels throughout the world. They are made in a wide range of sizes, depending on the type of water conditions they are to be fished in, which in turn affects their layout. In principle, the design of fykes is similar. The fyke net is a long, conical net supported by a variable number of cane, metal, or plastic hoops, with three or more internal funnels, each with a smaller opening than the preceding one. The first hoop, the largest, is horse-shoe shaped, so that it lies flat on the bottom, and is stable, while the remaining hoops are circular. This first hoop can be 40–400 cm in diameter, and the remaining hoops may taper down to as small as 20 cm.

The net is usually made of cotton, hemp of from a synthetic fibre, such as nylon, which is preferable as it has a longer working life. A 10 mm knot-to-knot mesh is used for the first few chambers of the cone, and the remainder may be of a 5 mm mesh. A fyke net can have both a leader and a wing net, which very effectively guide eels into the mouth of the first hoop of the net, and so further into the trap. The leader net projects from the middle of the first cone; is weighted at the base; fitted with floats on the top, and generally has a 10 mm knot mesh. The depth and length of the leader used depends on the water it is being fished in.

The fyke and leader, is set without any bait and generally at right angles to the shore or bank. The leader is secured close to the bank with a stake, and the fyke trap is furthest away from the bank. The height of the leader is generally the same as the depth of the water otherwise eels can swim over the top, thus reducing fishing efficiency. A feeding or migrating eel from either direction comes into contact with the leader, swims along it and into the fyke.

Alternatively, a fyke net may be fitted with two wing nets, which have the same function as a leader. They greatly increase the fishing efficiency, and are usually several feet in length, and set at right angles to one another from the mouth of the fyke net. The wing height is the same as that of both the fyke mouths and the water depth. A further device known as a guide net, which is anything up to 100 m in length, may be joined to one or both of the wing nets to further control the direction of an eel and increase the water area in which the net is effective. A combination of wing and guide nets can be set in such a way as to cover the whole river from bank to bank, so blocking the passage of every eel. The eel fyke trap should be as long as possible, so the eel loses contact with the first funnel before encountering the next one, otherwise possibly on making initial contact, it will back out and escape.

The correct and effective setting of leader, wing, and guide nets of a fyke, needs an intimate knowledge of local water conditions, and is outside the scope of this book, as there are so many layout permutations aimed at giving an eel the least possible chance of escape. Fykes are particularly successful in shallow estuaries in late summer, when eel movements are high, being set in the evening and emptied early the next morning. Fykes are, of course, usually of little use in deep of fast flowing waters.

Fykes are used extensively in Europe. In Holland, they are found all around Ijsselmeer, and in many canals; and in Denmark in shallow estuarine water all round the coastline. In France and Germany they are set in inland lakes and in rivers. The fyke net is generally recognised as one of the major factors influencing the rapid increase in eel capture and output in New Zealand, because of its high fishing efficiency in comparison with methods previously employed.

METHODS USED TO CATCH SILVER EELS

Silver eels are mostly caught at the beginning of their migration back to the Sargasso Sea. The timing of this movement usually coincides with heavy inland rains, and any fishing system used to capture silver eels must be able to withstand a considerable force of water, and be constructed in such a way as to catch migrating eels in the centre of the river, where the flow rate is at its highest. In some instances, despite the knowledge there are a large number of eels in a river, fishing is not possible as the downward force of water simply washes away any barrier which has been put up. Most silver eel fishing techniques involve permanent barriers which direct eels into a non-returnable V-trap. They are considerably more expensive to build than traps for brown eels, and there is always the risk, unless well sited, that everything can be swept away. To compensate for the high cost of construction, silver eels are considerably more valuable than brown eels. The following more important methods of silver eel capture are outlined: river weirs or barriers; yana; stow-nets; weir nets; fyke nets, and fixed fishing installations.

River Weirs or Barriers

There are numerous examples in Europe of river weirs or barriers being used to catch silver eels. Perhaps the best known system is on the River Bann, though they may be found in every European eel fishing country in some form or other. Permanent wooden weirs have been constructed across some of the canals leading from the Valli di Comacchio in Italy; and there are many old and now often unused barriers near water mill sites in England.

A barrier, as its name suggests, is an obstacle built across a river, stream, or canal, which a silver migrating eel or a brown migrating eel moving downstream cannot circumnavigate, and it is as a result forced into a collecting box. The effectiveness of a trap is considerably increased, if it is V-shaped, as both water and eels are forced towards one focal point. There may be either one or many V-constructions across a river. The number built depends on the width, and the force of a river and each V has its own collecting box. In some countries, legislation prohibits the building of weirs right across a river, so as to safeguard the movement of other species of fish. Gantries are built across most weirs to facilitate the lifting, and collection of trapped eels; and the checking of equipment.

A weir, as might be expected, is built when the water level is at its lowest level, during the summer months. They may be sited near the outflow of a lake, or a point where a river broadens out to become fairly level and shallow (80–130 cm deep) and where there is a good flow rate. A firm river base is, of course, preferable when building a permanent structure.

Most weirs are built of wood. Strong thick wooden stakes are driven into the river base at regular intervals to form a V, and are lined with wooden planks on the upstream side of the stakes. The final trap may be 2 m across at the entrance, and gradually taper into either a simple non-returnable fyke funnel, a collecting box, or a willow cane basket. In Madagascar, the local population build huts above the apex of the V-trap, and spear eels as they come into this area.

Weirs in Europe are fished mainly in August through until November. Catches, as outlined, are particularly high on dark and stormy nights, when a river is in flood. This raises one additional problem, that is debris being carried down by the river. This may easily block or break the trap rendering it ineffective, unless precautions are taken to release the pressure. In severe flooding, logs can act as battering rams, and smash the side guiding barriers. The collecting box should be constructed in such a way as to provide shelter for captured eels under such conditions, in order to prevent their being damaged by being pressed against the box lattice by the water current. In some cases the lattice work spacings of a collecting box is regulated by law, so as to allow the smaller eels to escape and grow on.

Yana

A yana, is a filtering method used in Japan for catching silver eels, and similar constructions are used in Europe on weirs or waterfalls. A long slanting wooden screen is placed across the river current. The downflowing water escapes through the slats on the screen, while the eels are retained, and are either washed up the slope of the screen by the water flow strength or wriggle up it in their attempt to escape. Yana may or may not be fitted with collecting boxes. If not, then a fisherman has to be available all the time to remove eels stranded on the screen during the main season.

Alternatively, a collecting channel can be built at the top of the screen, into which the eels fall, and then at a slight incline wriggle their way into a collecting box at the edge of the screen.

Stow Nets

Stow nets are another form of river barrier or weir, the only difference being a net in effect forms a V-barrier instead of wooden boards, and that they are temporary structures positioned only for the duration of the silver eel season, before being removed until the next. Stow nets are long cone shaped netbags, tapering into a non-returnable fyke-like collecting bag. The entrance to the netbag is mainly kept open by the force of the river flow, as only the entrance of the net is firmly held by a variety of devices. The net is usually suspended close to the river surface, as the silver eel migrates at this level, rather than at near the bottom of the river channel.

These types of nets are used either in swift running river water, or in strong tidal coastal regions. Three types of stow net are distinguishable according to the device by which the entrance of the net is kept open. These are: (a) stow nets at stakes, (b) stow nets at anchors, and (c) otter boards stow nets. The latter two are fixed to a boat or series of boats positioned across a river.

All three types of fixtures are used on German rivers, though the number found is decreasing annually. The problem is, stow nets should ideally be set in the middle of the river current in order to achieve maximum fishing efficiency, and this frequently conflicts with river transport. Leaves and other materials in the river, also build up in the stow nets.

Weir Nets
Most methods used to catch silver eels are a variation around one theme, and weir nets are no exception to the rule. A number of long conical nets can be positioned part or the whole way across a river, often set just below the outfall of inland waters with the net mouth facing upstream. These nets may be anything from 10–20 m long, with conical shaped traps or valves near the apex. The mesh size decreases from 6–7 cm from knot to knot at the entrance to 6 mm at the collecting end.

Live eel holding boxes are moored near the tails of the nets, and permanent staging and gantries may be rigged over the nets to make frequent emptying easier. A wall, fence, guide net or river bank can guide eels towards the entrance of the weir net, and usually a small part of the river width is left unobstructed to allow other fish to pass freely up and down. At the end of the season weir nets are lifted, dried, and stored until the next season.

The results of a series of experiments carried out in Ireland showed the number of eels caught increased as the net size used decreased. It appears it is better, therefore, to have a number of small V-weir nets set across a river, rather than only one or two large V-nets.

Fyke Nets

The design and method of setting fyke nets and supporting, wing, leader, and guide nets, has been outlined in methods used to catch brown eels. It is therefore sufficient to say fyke nets can equally well be used to catch silver eels, providing they are of a suitable size and strength for the river or estuary where they are being fished. They should not, however, be used in rivers where the flow rate and river depth are too great, as at the best of times it is extremely hard work lifting and setting fykes in the conditions under which silver eels normally migrate.

A guide net with buoys and weights can be set across a river, to direct silver eels towards the fyke positioned close to a bank. Sometimes a system of pulleys is set up on a bridge to raise and lower the fyke net for emptying without the operator having to struggle in the water. Some fishermen in Europe suspend lights across part of the river to help deflect silver eels from their original migration path towards the fyke trap.

Fixed Fishing Installations

In Italy, near the Po Delta and the Valli di Comacchio also in France, fixed fishing installations mounted on piers or small boats, are used to catch migrating brown or silver eels, and other types of fish. Each fishing unit is made up of a large square net, varying in size up to about 25 m × 25 m, which is raised and lowered by a series of pulleys and winches in and out of the water. The pulleys may be either hand operated or driven by a motor. Any fish caught are either scooped out of the centre of the net with a long handled scoop operated by the fisherman standing above on a pier, or released by untying a purse string into a boat positioned below the centre of the net.

Eels may be caught as they swim across the net, when it is lying flat on the bottom of a river. These nets, of course, cannot be used in fast flowing or uneven based rivers or canals. The net mesh size varies, decreasing towards the centre of the square. An individual square net may be made from four different overlapping mesh sizes varying from 3 cm to 6 mm from knot to knot. A light can be suspended above the net either to attract fish or to help clear the net of fish at night.

Fixed fishing installations may either cover only part of a river or channel, or may be mounted in such a way that they can be adjusted to take up any position across a river. Generally, these types of net are lowered into the middle of a river. There are perhaps as many as 1000 fixed fishing installations in France, and Italy, located along channels, rivers, cliffs, piers, jetties, and on boats.

EEL HOLDING AND TRANSPORTATION

The two previous sections outlined some of the various methods used to catch brown and silver eels in Europe and other parts of the world. It is, however, equally important to know how to handle, hold, and transport eels after they have been captured. All too often poor techniques used at this stage result in heavy losses of captured stock; so that the eels reach the market in a poor state of health. Quality, as well as quantity, as for any product, is an important aspect of marketing. Some eel merchants tend to overlook quality, and concentrate on quantity to the detriment of their potential and final income.

Holding Eels

The eel is rather unusual in comparison with other types of fish, in that unless it is to be frozen and shipped elsewhere, the vast majority are always marketed alive. This is firstly in part due to the eel's ability to survive in a limited amount of water by securing a large proportion of its oxygen needs by respiring through its skin, and secondly there is no way of establishing how long an eel has been dead or the circumstance of its death, if it is supplied dead. In any case, a dead eel soon begins to give off a repulsive smell. The market, therefore, in the majority of cases demands eel should be supplied alive.

A much higher price is paid by dealers for live eels, and some will only accept them if in such a state. It will be appreciated that both brown and silver eels are caught in fixed months of the year, give or take a week or two. The market at these times, like the cultured eel market, can be over supplied with eels, thereby reducing the price paid, as demand is limited. There are distinct advantages if live eels can be held, as it were, in 'cold storage' until the market price has improved. This is particularly true of silver eels, as the final price silver eel fishermen receive is, to a considerable extent, dependant on their skill in reading market trends. Certain annual festivals, such as those celebrated around Christmas in Italy, help build up demand, and make storage worthwhile.

A further reason for holding eels is to wait until a sufficiently large number have been accumulated to make it economical to transport them to market, or to have them picked up by a merchant. The number of eels captured whether they are brown or silver, is dependent on the prevailing weather conditions. They may be caught either slowly in 5–10 kg lots daily, or come suddenly in a 300–400 kg run. The fisherman must be prepared for both eventualities.

The quality of the eel product marketed is considerably enhanced if they are held alive in water for some time. This is especially true of brown eels which, prior to capture, will have been feeding along the river base. A period of 3–5 days allows these eels plenty of time to pass all their stomach food contents into the holding tanks, and for it to be washed away, rather than it being included in the sample at the market, and thereby producing a thoroughly off-putting smell, and leaving a repugnant muddy taste in the flesh. Brown eels should not, however, be held for too long otherwise their weight and condition begins to deteriorate rapidly. The same is not true for silver eels as at the time they are caught, they have ceased to feed and have large fat reserves.

Eels may be held either temporarily for a day to two, or permanently say for several months before being collected or marketed. All eel fishermen store newly caught eels in boxes or some sort of container close to where their traps are situated before they are transferred elsewhere. The boxes are usually rectangular in shape, covered in either 10 mm wire netting mesh, or made from wooden planks. They are suspended in the river, canal, or estuary, where the eels have been caught. Alternateively, eels may be stored in a tank built into the bottom of an old punt or boat moored near the nets.

The size of the holding box depends on the quantity of eels to be handled at any one time. This latter type of storage is applicable to the short term only, and to an individual eel fisherman's needs. These eels are regularly collected from these temporary holding tanks and transferred to larger long term tanks, if desired, where the catches of a number of eel fishermen are accumulated. Such larger tanks are used by live eel merchants or eel smokeries.

F

These tanks are elaborate structures and are suspended below a guarded floating platform which is tied up close to a smokery or distribution point. Ten or more tanks measuring $3 \times 2 \times 1$ m, made out of perforated metal sheeting may be suspended from one platform, which has a holding capacity for several 100 kg of eels. An aerator and pump may be used to increase the capacity of the tanks and the rate of water flow, when large numbers are being held at any one time.

Certain precautions must be observed with silver eels, particularly when only freshwater is available. Eels tend to get red disease, unless they occasionally have access to salt water. Some merchants, as a precaution, tow their eel platforms and holding tanks out to sea to expose them to salt water for a day or two every two weeks. Alternatively, salt is added to the tanks if it is not going to be too rapidly diluted. Man must, to a certain extent, simulate the conditions a silver eel encounters in its natural environment, if eels are to he held in a good condition.

Not all eels need be held in submerged tanks or boxes and some systems have been developed for use on land. Tanks similar to those outlined for holding elvers or those used at the beginning of the culture fattening process can also hold live eels, as in Japan and Taiwan, thereby helping to spread installation costs. The eels on arrival at the holding tanks are graded with the aid of tongs into large, small and medium sizes and divided into separate tanks. Care is taken to avoid any bruising and plenty of clean water is circulated through the tanks so as to avoid any fungal build up. Eels need relatively little additional oxygen by comparison to elvers, though adequate aeration should be provided. Eels always lie with their heads up. Dead eels are stinking eels, and must be removed from the tanks immediately. The inside of the tanks should be as smooth as possible to prevent any abrasion of the eels otherwise their ability to control their body salt content and resistance to fungal attack is impaired.

These eels, like those held on floating platforms, must have sufficient salt in the water to avoid bacterial disease building up. In order to keep the silver eels in good condition, the water circulation should be stopped every 10–14 days and the tanks drained until they are half empty. 20–25 kg of salt is than added to each tank, and the eels allowed to thrash around for 45 minutes and the slime to build up. At the end of this period the air and water circulation is turned full on again. As a rule, the longer silver eels are held alive after their natural run, the more money they are worth.

In Northern Italy, eels are held in containers suspended from a series of concrete arches over narrow fresh water channels built alongside the main catching barriers.

Eel Transportation

Live eels are transported varying distances by road, sea and air. The type of packaging method adopted is of course dependant on the type of transportation used. It is obviously totally un-economic to fly live eels held in water because of high air freight charges, therefore a more appropriate packaging method is chosen. This section is divided into road, sea, and air transportation for easy reference. The transportation of frozen dead eels is discussed under eel processing.

Road Transportation

Wooden boxes are widely used by Dutch eel fishermen and merchants to transport eels over relatively short distances, when the product is to be marketed almost immediately on receipt. It is not possible to hold eels for any length of time without some water, and the period they can be held in boxes is further reduced when outside temperatures rise, as wooden boxes offer little insulation. Most eel movements using this method are made in the early hours of the day while it is still cool.

Four to five divided individual wooden trays, measuring 100 × 40 × 8 cm with perforated bottoms, are placed inside a large wooden box fitted with carrying handles on either end. Generally, five to six eels are placed in each tray compartment depending on their individual weights. In total each large wooden box contains 15–20 kg of eels. Sometimes ice is placed in the top tray, so that moisture gradually filters through the trays during transportation, so keeping the eels moist and cool. Eels survive for up to 24 hours under this system with little or no loss and each complete unit now costs about £10.

A number of eel merchants use polystyrene boxes, as opposed to wooden boxes, and this improves the flexibility of this method of packaging. The boxes measure 100 × 50 × 40 cm and are easy to handle, lightweight, insulated, returnable, and do not require any specialist support equipment such as air compressors. 8–10 kilos of eels are placed in each box together with sufficient water on the bottom to keep the eels moist and cool, with a perforated lid placed on top to allow some aeration.

The majority of live eels transported by road are held in water in special container tanks mounted on lorries. Water containers are mainly used during the summer months, when the outside air temperature is relatively high and there is a danger eels will dehydrate. Eels may be transported much longer distances and in larger quantities under this method. A regular distribution service is maintained by the Northern Ireland eel co-operatives to England and Europe using this technique.

The finer details of the exact design of holding tanks, generators, and aerators used on lorries varies from merchant to merchant and from country to country. In outline, the tanks are made either of fibre glass, which offers some degree of insulation, or of galvanised steel. Up to five or six tanks are mounted on the rear of a lorry, each measuring approximately 2 × 1 × 1 m, and are securely fastened to the base of the lorry floor at either end. An access hatch with a retaining lip is situated on the top of the tank to enable eels and water to be added.

A fine mesh plate with small circular holes is fitted near the base of each tank. Under this plate there is a system of perforated tubes through which air is continuously blown during transportation, in order to maintain the aeration at a sufficiently high level under high stocking density conditions. The plate prevents the eels from coming into direct contact with this system. As a rule each lorry is fitted with two air compressor pumps. One is actually used and the other serves as a standby in case the first one breaks down, otherwise a whole consignment of highly valuable fish could be lost.

Each tank has a water drainage point fitted at the base enabling the tanks to be completely drained and cleaned out between consignments. Eels are quickly and easily removed on arrival at their destination through a hatch fitted just above the plate level on each tank. The hatch door is opened, a control shield lifted, and eels allowed to flow down a trough into suitable holding containers at the market or collecting point. The system outlined depends on a continual flow of air during transportation. In addition, more elaborate and hence more efficient systems involve a continual circulation of water through the tanks. This is maintained by a small diesel pump and a standby.

The volume of water in each tank is kept to a minimum, while still being completely effective, otherwise transportation costs per unit weight of eels is considerably increased. In practice, each tank is filled to about one third to a half with eels, and the remainder of the area is taken up with water. Live eels create a considerable amount of foam when first put into a tank, so water is allowed to overflow for some time while the tank is being filled to clear away as much foam as possible. The eels quieten down after a relatively short time with their heads on the water surface. A safety net can be placed on top of the tank while it is being filled.

It is better to have a number of small tanks on each lorry, rather than just one large tank, from the viewpoint that eels and the tanks will be easier to handle and a loss in one tank will not (hopefully) spread to another tank. As many as 12 small tanks may be fitted on one lorry. Live eels are usually transported at night when it is cool and on arrival at their destination they are spread out as soon as possible.

The initial cost of such a transportation system, once a suitable lorry, compressors, and tanks have been purchased, is high by comparison with other transportation systems. These costs can, however, be spread either over a large number of eels as each full load may weigh 1–1,2 tonnes, alternatively, the same system can be used for transportation of elvers or other species of fish.

Sea Transportation
Sea transportation of eels follows much the same principles as road transportation. Specially built tanks with perforated sides and bottoms are built into boats and are fitted with water pumps and aeration equipment. A number of changes of water can, of course, be affected so eels can be held indefinitely in these tanks.

The hulls of some boats are perforated to allow water to pass through into compartments containing the eels. Eels held in these types of vessels are exposed to the surrounding water and possible pollution. It has been known for whole consignments of eels to be lost in this way.

Air Transportation

Improved market prices and demand in recent years have made it an economic proposition to air freight live eels to certain markets, despite their value per unit weight being lower than that for elvers. Ten kilos of live eels are placed in a polythene bag with 1 kilo of ice and a small quantity of oxygen from a cylinder and closed with a rubber band. Two such bags are placed in a waxed cardboard box which is then sealed up. The eels occupy about half the total space while the remainder is taken up by oxygen. This system is widely used in Taiwan to transport live eels to Japan and in America to transport eels to Europe.

The ice reduces the respiration rate of the eels and keeps them moist throughout the trip. This system can only be used for a relatively short length of time (up to 36 hours) before all the oxygen in the bag is absorbed and the eels begin to die. The oxygen cannot be replaced by atmospheric oxygen, as the bag is sealed.

Fig 57 A small fyke net with U shaped
front hoop, and buoyed and weighted
guiding net.

Fig 58 A fyke net staked out at right
angles to a fake bank.

Fig 59 Aboard an eel longline boat
equipped with marker buoys, hook and
line boxes.

Fig 60 The eel market in Copenhagen, Denmark.

Fig 61 A bulk eel lorry fitted with three holding tanks, and loaded with wooden boxes in Holland.

Fig 62 Wooden eel boxes and trays dry in the sun after use.

Section 4–Eel Processing

INTRODUCTION
The simplest definition of animal food processing is the conversion of one body form into another. Generally speaking the result is a product which has increased saleability and or edibility. Processing is of particular importance in the successful marketing of eels, as the majority of eels are sold to consumers in either one processed form or another – as smoked or jellied eels, or as kabyaki – as opposed to being sold alive. This section as Fig 19 shows, outlines in turn all the stages involved in the processing of cultured and captured eels and includes information on how to kill, gut, clean, freeze, cold store, brine, smoke, pack, glaze, and jelly eels, as well as how to prepare kabyaki.

Processing should not however be thought to be solely confined to commercial ventures of one form or another. The housewife, when she purchases a live eel will, in her own right, technically process an eel to produce a dish for the enjoyment of her family. A surprisingly wide range of dishes using eels is outlined at the end of this section. These are taken from *Larousse Gastronomique* and any reader whose imagination is stirred by the names of some of these dishes is advised to refer to this excellent and well known publication for further details on their preparation.

Killing
All stages leading up to the killing of eels have been discussed in previous sections. The actual intentional killing of an eel generally takes place either in the market place or at the 'factory' where they are to be processed, whether it be for smoking, jellying or freezing. There are two widely used methods for killing eels though there are a number of other more localised methods.

The first and simplest method is to put eels into a deep container together with a handful of salt for each 5 kg of eels, which is sufficient to cover them but not enough to completely bury them, otherwise the eels die too quickly. The eels thrash around together for up to two hours, gradually absorbing more and more salt,

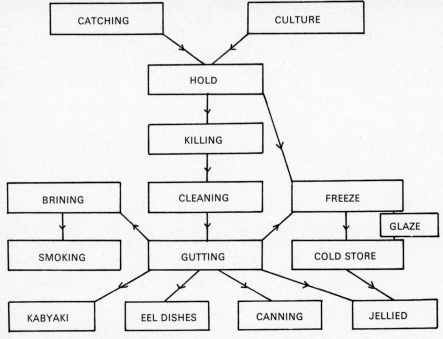

Fig 19   Some stages in processing eels

and eventually die. This method has the advantage that much of the undesirable slime normally covering eels is removed enabling them to be handled with greater ease, and it is particularly appropriate for the preparation of eels for smoking. Up to five per cent of their bodyweight can be lost during this stage.

It is not, however, always desirable that eels should be slowly killed in a salt bath. The second method using an electrical current is a more popular method. Eels on arrival at the processing plant are placed in a suitably large holding bin with some fresh water and a current of up to 500 volts is passed for several minutes through the container until all the eels are stunned. The eels can be restunned if necessary. This method is a quick, easy, and a clean way of killing eels though, of course, appropriate precautions must be taken when using electricity. There are a number of other less humane and desirable methods. Some processors dispense with electrical stunning altogether and simply place live eels in container blocks before putting them straight into a freezer unit.

In the preparation of kabyaki, live eels are pinned through their heads to a wooden board, slit open down the side of their backs and their guts and backbones removed. This is all done very swiftly, as one would hope. A number of European eel merchants skin live eels once a customer has made a selection. An insertion is made just behind the head, extended round the head, the skin raised and then pulled back down the body (rather like taking a stocking off). The skinned eel then dies slowly.

Cleaning

The cleaning of an eel is generally referred to as desliming as opposed to gutting. Much of the slime will have been removed already if the eel has been killed in salt. If an alternative killing method is used, then eels can be immersed in a one per cent ammonia solution made up by adding one part of ammonia liquor to 100 parts of water, which rapidly removes any protective slime. Alternatively freshly killed and selected eels can be washed, scrubbed, and carefully scraped by hand in clean water to remove all traces of slime and then rinsed in fresh water. By this time they should feel clean and firm to the grasp. The continuing presence of slime on an eel leaves a white undesirable precipitation on the skin of a smoked eel.

Gutting

Eels are de-gutted before being smoked, jellied or prepared for kabyaki. However, live eels are not gutted immediately in all instances. Some buyers specify eels should not be gutted before they are frozen for shipment. To gut an eel, a slit is made in its belly an inch or so beyond the anus vent, and the knife is passed up through the belly to the head. An incision at this point ensures the kidney is removed. Care must be taken not to cut through the gall bladder, otherwise the flesh can become tainted. The cut cavity is then scrubbed, scraped, and washed out to remove all traces of blood from the backbone and throat. Then finally the eels are rinsed out. Gutting results in a body weight loss of five to ten per cent.

Sawdust or salt can be sprinkled on the eel to enable the worker to handle the eel with greater ease. The head and skin are not removed for smoking. A few large scale processors use mechanical gutting machines to make an incision along the length of the eel before the contents of the body cavity are sucked out. The variable size of eels and the difficulty of maintaining them in the correct position, however, limits the widespread use of mechanical equipment for gutting.

Freezing

Eels may be frozen either if they are not going to be processed immediately after cleaning and gutting, or after they have been processed, or while still alive or stunned with their guts still intact. They may be either frozen in blocks or individually.

One method of freezing used to export frozen whole eels is to place suitable stunned and graded eels in a plastic bag lining a galvanised steel mould. Approximately 8–10 kg of eels are placed in each mould and a tight fitting lid is placed on the top. In this state the moulds are transferred to racks in a blast freezer and frozen at − 40°F for 18 hours. The mould is made the same size as the carton the eels are to be packaged in for shipment as this considerably improves ease of handling.

After freezing, two moulds of frozen eels are placed in a second larger plastic bag in an unwaxed cardboard box, wired up and transferred, until shipment, to a cold storage unit. In this way 16–20 kg of eels are packed with ease in each box. A corrugated cardboard box is used in preference to plain cardboard in that it is a better insulator and results in the product only slightly thawing out when it is being handled outside during shipment.

An alternative to block freezing eels in plastic bags within moulds, is to place the eels in their final transportation cardboard box at the outset and then freeze them. In practice, this causes the box to become distorted and bulge which makes them difficult to stack, thereby wasting much valuable freight space.

Gutted eels may be frozen in blocks in trays using a horizontal plate freezer, which is essentially the same technique as outlined for a galvanised steel mould. Eels should be frozen within 12 hours of killing. Many people recommend they should not be frozen ungutted otherwise sometimes the normal white flesh of the eel is discoloured with blood. However, this discoloration generally occurs when the eel has been frozen too rapidly and an internal haemorrhage has resulted. Unfortunately, this can go undetected until the eel reaches the market.

Glazing

Some buyers specify eels should be glazed, so as to improve their quality and presentation. Glazing is done before freezing so that freeze burns, which can appear on the eel's skin while they are being frozen, are avoided. In this way each individual eel has a protective layer around it. In its stunned state a hook is pushed through the eel's lower jaw. It is then dipped in cold water, hung up, and cold air is blasted through the freezing chamber. If an eel is dipped several times, a better glaze is produced which makes an improvement to the market presentation of the product.

Pushing a hook through an eel's jaw can be a time consuming and labour intensive process. An effective alternative requiring less time is to keep the eel in water and then lay it along corrugated plastic sheeting or some other such material. Using this method the eel remains as rigid and straight as those glazed while hanging up. After an eel has been glazed it is packed in its consignment carton or mould and frozen.

Cold Storage

Frozen processed or unprocessed eels can be cold stored satisfactorily in much the same way as other fish. Cold storage facilities enable the producer and processor both to release eels onto the market when prices offered are favourable and to store eels bought in cheaply, or caught seasonally. Eels have a high fat content and should, therefore, be well protected against rancidity and drying out. They are stored ideally at a relatively low temperature of $-29°C$ $(-20°F)$. Eels should keep in good condition for at least six months, when correctly frozen and stored at this temperature and if stored at $-34°C$ $(-30°F)$ they can be kept for at least twelve months. However, some eels stored longer than nine months begin to taint and lose some of their colour. There would appear to be few advantages in keeping them longer otherwise they will begin to compete unequally with fresh eels caught in the new season.

Cartons of frozen eels are generally stacked on pallets and direct contact with the cold storage wall is avoided by the use of partition boarding.

Brining

Brining is a preliminary preparatory stage carried out before eels are smoked and is important in ensuring eels that are smoked have the right taste. Either freshly killed or thawed out eels can be used. In outline, eels are placed in a salt solution, the concentration of which and the length of time they are immersed in it varies according to the experience of an individual processor, and differences in consumer market taste. Some processors recommend small eels should be placed in a ten per cent brine solution for ten minutes, whereas larger eels should be immersed for half an hour. A concentration of brine of this strength is made up by adding 1 lb of salt to one gallon of water, for every 10 lbs of eels. After brining eels are thoroughly rinsed.

Other processors recommend eels should be immersed in an 80 per cent saturation brine solution for ten minutes using $2\frac{3}{4}$ lbs of salt in one gallon of water. A brinometer should be used to gauge the percentage level of saturation. In theory, the heavier the brining that is used, the longer is the product's shelf life. Excessive brining, however, results in white spots appearing on the skin of the eel during smoking and can also cause the product to become unacceptable because of too strong a taste of salt.

Vacuum dried salt is always used to make up a brine solution as other types of salt can contain undesirable impurities. Dry salt should never be used at this stage. As a rule a brine solution is used only for one day then discarded, otherwise bacteria can build up.

Smoking

The techniques used to smoke eel vary almost without exception from processor to processor making it quite impossible to give an exact description on how to best smoke eels. The subject, however, can be conveniently discussed in outline both in terms of the equipment needed to smoke eels and in terms of the smoking technique. Any would-be eel smoker is well advised to begin on a trial scale before adopting a full scale processing system. Eels are usually hot smoked after brining. This method generally involves relatively sophisticated equipment which may be beyond the means of a person intending to undertake a comparatively small scale operation. So a low cost alternative operation is outlined for this reason.

The first type of smoking kiln recommended for hot smoking eels involves the use of both gas heating and steam. The kiln can be built from brick but more frequently it is made out of sheet metal. The walls are double with a $1\frac{1}{4}''$ layer of insulation between them and the whole unit may measure $7' 4'' \times 3' 7'' \times 3' 7''$ or a little over $2\,m \times 1\,m \times 1\,m$. The cabinet is heated by gas burners of which there may be up to seven on the floor of each kiln. Each burner is capable of consuming 36 cu ft of gas per hour. Special air inlets are provided on the feed pipe to each burner which can be regulated, as required, to supply fresh air to the flame when all other air supply inlets to the kiln are closed. There may also be a pilot light arrangement to ensure the gas is re-ignited should the flame go out during any stage of the process due to draughts created by the too rapid opening and closing of the doors, or because of any other reason.

The individual gas jets ignite and burn a mixture of wood wool and wood chips of oak or other broad leaved timbers contained in wire mesh baskets resting on the fire bars above the burners. This mixture can be blanketed as desired with sawdust or peat. The temperature inside the kiln is automatically controlled by thermostats, though it is possible to obtain a first class product without the use of them. A quick reading thermometer with a range of $0-150\,^\circ C$ is, however, an essential piece of equipment.

The steam is produced by a separate copper steam boiler located near the kilns and is introduced through an inlet at the base of the kiln at certain stages of this particular process. Steam rapidly produces conditions of high temperature and humidity as and when required.

An overhead rail is fastened to the underside of the roof of each kiln and projects out in front of it. A trolley car is suspended from a wheeled bogey which runs on this rail and it is possible to move this unit with ease either into the kiln with freshly prepared eels for smoking, or to the adjoining cooling room with newly smoked eels. The trolley from which the eels are suspended is free to rotate about the point of suspension from the bogey and is made out of lengths of light gauge angle iron. Those pieces placed horizontally along the upper edge of the trolley are serrated so that the light gauge steel rods carrying eels from one side to the other firmly rest upon them without any danger of movement when the cage is being moved. This ensures an eel hanging from a rod cannot touch any on an adjoining rod which might result in them sticking together and so spoiling the finished product. The bottom of each trolley is covered with a wire mesh grille or a sheet of expanded metal to prevent insecurely held eels from falling into the fire.

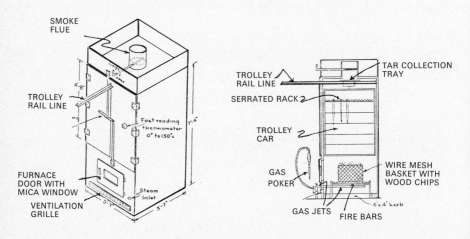

GAS AND STEAM SUPPLY NOT SHOWN

Fig 20   Outline of hot smoking kiln design

Eels carefully selected according to size are impaled on stainless steel rods through the back of the head and out through the underside, slightly in front of the dorso-ventral fin. Up to twelve eels, depending on their size are threaded onto each rod. Once a full complement is reached the rod is placed on the supports provided for this purpose on each side of the trolley car. The steel rods vary in size from about $\frac{3}{16}''$ diameter, used for holding small sized eels, to about $\frac{3}{8}''$ diameter for larger eels, or are of that size which is necessary to support eels without the rod sagging. Additional support is provided by hooks for larger eels, where necessary. These reduce the strain of the weight of the eel on the part impaled thereby avoiding the eel breaking apart at the support and falling down. The hooks are made of steel wire bent to the necessary shape so that one end can be hooked over and be supported by the rod carrying the eels, while the other end is inserted in the body. In addition, small lengths of stick can be placed between the belly flaps to keep them apart, thereby allowing smoke to penetrate the cavity more easily.

Each trolley car, when loaded with eels, should be capable of holding up to 100 kilos which could amount to 400 or more eels being smoked at any one time. Some trolleys are built in such a way that two layers of eel can be suspended from them at any one time. Whether both layers are used at the same time depends very much of the skill of the smoker, as those eels on the lower level will tend to cook more quickly than those on the upper layer.

Before the trolley loaded with eels is placed inside the kiln, all the doors and air inlets are closed and the temperature is raised to 110°C. The trolley is then wheeled into the kiln which results in the temperature falling. This is then quickly brought back up to 90–95°C for smaller eels, and up to 105°C for larger eels. Sometimes, however, if the temperature is raised too quickly the eels may become hard cased, particularly when their fat content is low. The skin then becomes dry and hard, while the flesh remains very wet.

Steam is introduced for about three minutes when a temperature of 105°C has been reached so that the incision in the belly of the eel gapes wide apart. Water can be sprinkled on the fire bars if insufficient steam is being produced. The object is to cook the eel as quickly as possible so as to keep to a minimum the loss in weight which occurs in this part of the process without, at the same time, subjecting the eel to an excessively high temperature which could cause the body to curve. Alternatively, if an eel is smoked at a lower temperature for a prolonged period, it could result in the eel breaking away from its support.

After steam has been passed for the required time all air vents are opened and the steam is cut off. The temperature is maintained at or about 90°C for a period of 10–15 minutes for small eels and 100–105°C for 20–30 minutes for larger eels. Steam may again be introduced into the kiln during this stage of the process when large eels are being smoked. This ensures heat penetrates quickly into the flesh and thereby reduces the weight loss. If this method is used it is necessary, however, to start at a temperature of lower than 100–105°C in order to prevent the eel from breaking apart.

Throughout the smoking period a close watch on the smoke produced is kept though a mica inspection window. Additional peat or sawdust is added as and when required to ensure the production of a large volume of smoke, and to prevent the outbreak of a bright flame from the wood chippings. At the end of this 10–30 minute period, the eels should be evenly brown, tender, supple and have a good smoky flavour with only a slight taste of salt. The flesh under the skin should be a light pink and soft to the touch, while the body cavity is browned.

At the end of the process eels are removed from the kiln and allowed to cool completely before they are packed, otherwise undesirable moulds may appear. Some smokeries brush the eels lightly with vegetable oil to improve their presentation gloss. As a guideline, the temperature of eel flesh must be brought up to 60°C or more before it can be offered for human consumption. This is more than adequately reached during the hot smoking process. The loss of body weight can be quite considerable during smoking and may amount to anything up to 25 per cent, though the level naturally depends on the skill of the smoker.

The second type of smoking kiln recommended is a Torry mechanical kiln which does not usually use steam or such high cooking temperatures. The process, therefore, takes longer to complete. The preparation of the eels for the trolleys is exactly the same as outlined above. This method is most suitable for eels weighing 350–700 g ($\frac{3}{4}$–1$\frac{1}{2}$ lbs) though heavier eels as well can be cooked successfully.

Table 27 – Processing time for different weight eels

	350–700 g ($\frac{3}{4}$–1$\frac{1}{2}$ lb) eels		Up to 2$\frac{1}{4}$ kg (5 lbs)	
	Time (hr)	Temp (°C)	Time (hr)	Temp (°C)
	1	35	1$\frac{1}{2}$	35
	$\frac{1}{2}$	49	1	50
	1	77	2	80
Total	2$\frac{1}{2}$		Total 4$\frac{1}{2}$	

The third type of kiln suggested is more primitive costing well under £100 to build while still producing a perfectly acceptable product. The kiln can be made from breeze blocks and fitted with metal doors. A simple frame attached to the wall at a suitable level carries the suspended rods of eels. Oak is used to light the fire on the floor of the kiln which may then be damped down with sawdust. A grid above the fire prevents the eels from falling into it, while a tray above the eels stops wood tar on the roof from falling onto the eels. All kilns have a controlled chimney exit to regulate the rate of outflow of smoke. A regular check can easily be made on how well the eels are cooking.

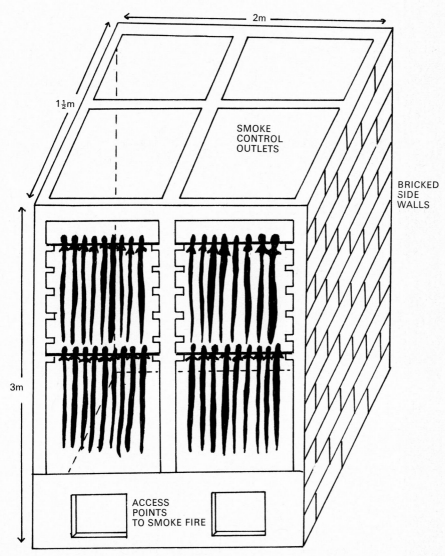

Fig 21   Design for simple home made kiln

There are a number of other general points which should be remembered when smoking eels. It is best to use mixed hardwood for the process. Resinous woods, such as pine, are never used. All sawdust and wood chippings must be checked to make sure there are no solvents in them, especially when a chain saw has been used, otherwise the smell of the petrol/oil mixture will be passed on to the eels. Oak, if available, is the most widely used fuel. It is not possible to hot smoke fillets of eels, as the flesh breaks down. Eels are always smoked whole and then filleted if desired by the market.

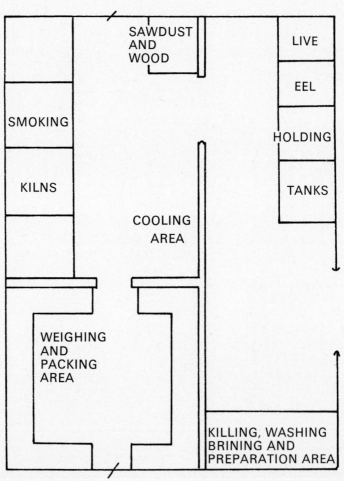

Fig 22   Layout of a smokery

No vegetable oil is used either before or during the process as the eel itself produces sufficient fat from its own body tissues.

The most important point to make is that any smoking process adopted must suit the available eels and the local consumer taste. A great deal of information can be acquired from others before launching an expensive operation. Some eels, such as New Zealand eels, have a lower fat content than the European eel and there is a danger that the product can dry out if it is overheated. There is also a considerable variation in the size of smoked eels demanded by different European countries.

No discussion on the eel smoking process is complete without outlining the layout of a smokery and its auxiliary facilities. Fig 22 clearly shows without need of further explanation what these facilities should include.

Table 28 – Summary of weight loss during processing

Stage	Percentage loss
Desliming	5
Gutting	5–10
Smoking	15–20
Total weight loss	25–35

The appreciable shrinkage and loss of weight during the smoking process should be taken into account when calculating wholesale and retail prices.

Jellied Eels

The majority of processed eels in the world are smoked. The only other process of any significance is jellying, which is confined mainly to Southern England and Holland. It seems unlikely any reader would be considering starting a jellied eel processing plant because of the very limited demand for such a product. In England there are now only three or four firms still specialising in producing this product. However, this section is included so as to give a complete and fully comprehensive coverage of processing. The details of the processing technique, as with smoked eel, vary from processor to processor and the information outlined is intended only to provide a guideline.

Both fresh or frozen eels can be used. Cold storage facilities enable a processor to buy in frozen imported eels more cheaply than those freshly caught locally. There is, however, a distinct preference in the trade for fresh eels even though frozen eels offer a potentially higher profit margin. The eels are gutted and cleaned in the manner previously outlined and all the final traces of gut and blood veins are removed. Next the gutted eels is cross sliced by hand into pieces about 4–5 cms ($1\frac{1}{2}$–2 inches) long, and there may be as many as 30 slices to a pound. The head is removed. The sliced eel is then placed in a shallow tray together with the juices exuded while being cut. These trays are positioned inside a block freezer and the temperature set at $-40°$C ($-40°$F). In such manner a number of blocks of frozen sliced eels are prepared prior to being thawed out and used to produce jellied eels. Frozen blocks provide a very convenient way to store eels. It may be advisable to pass the pieces of eel over a metal detector before processing to make sure eels caught on long lines no longer have any hooks embedded in their flesh or mouths.

Freshly prepared or thawed out pieces of eel are then cooked by placing them in boiling water. The water is brought to the boil and about 450 g (one lb) of salt for every 11 kg (25 lbs) of eel is added. The pieces simmer until the flesh is soft enough to be pushed off the bone with the fingers. The cooking time varies according to the size of the eel, the season of the year, the area of capture, and the species of the eel. The New Zealand eel, for instance, needs to be boiled a little longer than the European eel before the meat drops off the bone, The dorsal and ventral fins are also larger than those of its European counterpart which makes them less suitable for this type of processing. The skin is usually removed from these eels for jellying purposes. Brown eels usually need to be boiled for ten minutes, whereas silver eels (which have thicker, tougher skins) require longer and should be overcooked rather than undercooked.

Once the cooking is completed, cold water is added to the cooking container which brings the fat to the surface so that it can be easily skimmed off. The cooked pieces and hot liquor are then poured into large bowls containing gelatine dissolved in a small amount of hot water and usually made up as a ten per cent solution. Sometimes a small amount of vinegar is also added to help bring out the flavour. The concentration of the gelatine solution used depends on the condition of the eels and their natural ability to gel. As a guideline, five pounds of gutted eel produce five pounds of jellied eel.

When the mixture has cooled, the pieces of eel and jelly are either placed in individual waxed carton pots for resale or are put into larger metal bowls. Ideally, there should be a few 'floaters' or segments of eel on the surface of the jelly to improve market presentation. Waxed carton packs may have a shorter shelf life than other containers since there is sometimes a reaction between the gelatine and wax coating. Silver eels are preferred by the trade as they have a beautiful silvery colour which improves their appearance in the dishes. Their meat is also better.

Another recipe for jellied eels recommends the use of a salt-vinegar solution. Water containing 2 per cent vinegar and 3 per cent salt, together with 2 ozs of spices to the gallon, is brought to the boil and 2 inch pieces of eel are added. The mixture is brought back to the boil and then left to simmer for about 45 minutes. The pieces are then put in bowls to cool and a weak gelatine solution is added, if there is insufficient natural jelly.

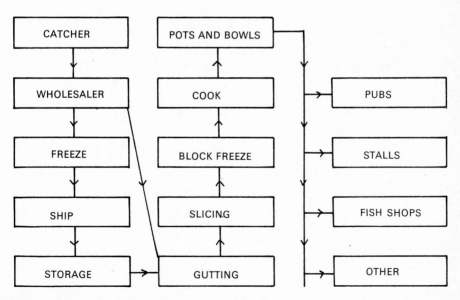

Fig 23   Stages in the jellied eel processing and marketing chain

Jellied eel processing is therefore a question of local skill and know-how on how to produce exactly the right taste for customers. The final magical ingredient or technique is handed down from generation to generation and kept as a carefully guarded secret not to be given away. Of the two main forms of eel processing, it is possibly easier for a beginner to achieve a quality smoked eel, rather than a jellied product.

Canned Eels

There is a very limited world wide trade in both canned smoked and jellied eels as consumers, at present, apparently prefer freshly prepared eel products. The initial preparation of eels for canning is exactly the same as previously outlined. Eels, if a Torry kiln is being used, are smoked for one hour at 35°C (95°F), one hour at 49°C (120°F), and finally for one hour at 77°C (170°F), these are slightly higher temperatures than those used for other eel smoking processes using the same equipment. The eels are then removed from the kiln and allowed to cool before being cut into pieces according to the size of the cans being used. Canned smoked eels should be both skinless and boneless and be preserved in their own natural jelly, if possible. Alternatively, once the pieces have been packed in the can, the remaining space if filled with vegetable oil heated to 110°C (230°F). The cans are then sealed and heat processed at 110°C (230°F). A seven oz oval can takes about one hour to cook. Canned smoked eel is served sliced and garnished with lemon.

In the preparation of canned jellied eels, pieces of skinned eel can be partly boiled for about 10 minutes in water containing two per cent vinegar, three per cent salt, and two ozs of spices to the gallon. After this time the cooked pieces are drained, cooled, and packed either in glass or flat cans. A ten per cent gelatine solution, containing one per cent acetic acid and a few drops of lemon essence, is then added. The containers are vacuum sealed and heat processed at 120°C (248°F) and $2\frac{1}{4}$ kg (5 lbs) pressure. An 8 oz pack needs about 30 minutes, whereas a 1 lb pack requires about one hour of heating.

Kabayaki

Kabayaki is a traditional Japanese gourmet dish prepared from eels. It assumes a high level of importance in that it is in this form that a very large proportion of the big tonnage of home cultured and imported eels is consumed. This dish, however, is rarely found in Europe except, of course, in Japanese restaurants. Generally, kabayaki is eaten freshly prepared either in special restaurants in Tokyo and the main cities or at home. More recently, a number of kabayaki processing factories have been built in Shizouka Prefecture to produce a prepacked product, which has stimulated renewed interest in eel culture for processing.

In restaurants, kabayaki is prepared by pinning out a live eel onto a wooden board. The eel is slit open with a sharp knife, and the stomach contents and backbone removed. In effect the eel is filleted to produce a number of 10–12 cm long pieces of meat. Next several bamboo skewers or metal needles are threaded through each fillet to keep the flesh flat while it is being grilled. The Japanese prefer their own species of eel for kabayaki as opposed to the European eel. The longer narrower body shape is more suitable for cutting into fillets than that of the European eel, which tends to be shorter and wider and produces less fillets per eel.

Carefully prepared fillets on skewers are then taken through a series of cooking sequences. First, boiling water is poured over them, on the skin side, then on the flesh side, before they are held over steam and lightly cooked. Next they are dipped in soya sauce and grilled over charcoal. The dipping and grilling is repeated several times to produce a crisp, succulent dish flavoured with soya which easily falls apart in the mouth.

Eel Dishes

This book in no way sets out to be regarded partly as a cookery guide. However, an appreciation of the very wide range of dishes which can be prepared from eels may help producers and merchants to stimulate increased consumer interest in eels. A housewife's awareness of the flexibility of the product, and a careful presentation of the product and cooking guide, can increase demand and sales. The 57 different eel dishes listed are in the main taken from *Larousse Gastronomique*. It is to this book that any interested reader should be referred. Bon Appetite!

The following dishes can be prepared from eels: Anguilles à l'Anglaise; Ballottine d'Anguille; Ballottine d'Anguille froide; Saucission d'Anguille; Anguille Farcie a la gelée; Ballottine

169

d'Anguille Chaude; Ballottine d'Anguille à l'Ancienne; Ballottine d'Anguille à la Bourguignonne; Ballottine d'Anguille à la Gauloise; Bastion d'Anguille; Anguille à la Bonne Femme; Roulade d'Anguille froide; Roulade d'Anguille à l'Angevine; Roulade d'Anguille à la Bordelaise; Roulade d'Anguille à la Royale; Coulibiac d'Anguille; Petits Coulibiacs d'Anguille; Anguille à la Creme, au Paprika; Anguille à la Diable; Anguille à la Fermière; Anguille en Fricassée; Anguille frite; Anguille frite Orly; Galantine d'Anguille en Volute; Anguille Grillée Maître d'Hotel; Anguille à l'Italienne; Anguille en matelote; Anguille en matelot à la Normande; Anguille à la Meunière; Pâté Chaud d'Anguille à l'Anglaise; Pâté chaud d'Anguille aux fines herbes dite à la Ménagère; Pâté chaud d'Anguille à la Nantua; Pâté chaud d'Anguille aux Truffes; Pâté froid d'Anguille à l'Anglaise; Pâté froid d'Anguille à la Ménagère; Pâté froid d'Anguille à la Nantua; Pâté froid d'Anguille aux Truffes; Anguilles à la Piémontaise Anguille à la Poulette; Anguille à la Provençale; Anguille à la Romaine; Anguille en Brochette à l'Anglaise; Anguille à la Tartare; Tourte Chaude d'Anguille; Tourte froide d'Anguille Rabelais; Anguille à la Tyrolienne; Anguilles au vert; Anguille Villeroi; Anguilles nicoises; Anguille Fumées; Anguilles à l'escouvêche; eels on skewers; grilled eels; steamed egg and eel squares; grilled eels on rice; marinated eels; and stewed eels.

Fig 63 Eels are held in bulk in easily removed nets at the market in Denmark.

Fig 64 Eel holding boxes temporarily store live eels outside a smokery in Holland.

Fig 65 Freshly prepared smoked eels.

Fig 66 The final stage in the marketing chain. A length of smoked eels being packed for a customer.

Section 5–Eel Marketing

INTRODUCTION

Details of the elver market in terms of origin of supply, quantities and prices involved have been discussed in Section One, and the marketing of cultured eels has likewise been outlined in Section Two, as part of eel culture. This section by contrast deals solely with the marketing of captured wild brown and silver eels, though regrettably there are no figures available which differentiate between the quantities marketed of these two types of eel.

The successful marketing of any product depends to a large extent on having relevant up-to-date facts about a product and its market. There is a wide variation in approach to the collection and analysis of relevant facts and market information. Some may only collect the bare minimum of information whereas others will delve into all available sources for facts. This section therefore may contain much too much detailed information for some readers whereas for others, it will contain insufficient data. More detailed specific data, if required, can be found by referring to the references given or by contacting firms involved in eel marketing who may be prepared to divulge the relevant information.

The factual aspects of eel marketing are analysed in terms of the weight of different species of wild eels caught in the five years (1968–1973); the value of this catch in US dollars; the value of the catch in the currency of the country of capture; and eel exports from principal exporting countries. These figures are taken from the different issues of *FAO Yearbook of Fishery Statistics* relating to catchings and landings, and fishery commodities.

Finally a few notes are included outlining the variable eel requirements of different European countries. It must be stressed immediately that no responsibility can be accepted for the comprehensiveness of these notes and the list though it is hoped they will give the reader a valuable introduction and guideline to this market.

WEIGHT OF WILD EELS CAUGHT ANNUALLY ('000 tons)

The figures listed in Tables 29–32 are given in terms of thousands of metric tons:

A. European eel

Table 29 – Weight of European eels caught (1969–1974)

Country/year	1969	1970	1971	1972	1973	1974
Denmark	3.7	3.4	3.2	3.3	3.6	2.9
France	1.9	4.2	4.9	2.6	3.9	2.5
Germany (Fed.)	0.5	0.5	0.5	0.4	0.4	0.4
Germany (Dem.)	1.0	1.1	0.8	0.9	0.9	0.9
S. Ireland	0.1	0.2	0.1	0.1	0.1	0.1
Italy	3.4	3.2	3.3	2.8	2.9	2.7
Netherlands	2.8	1.5	1.2	1.1	1.1	1.0
Norway	0.5	0.4	0.4	0.4	0.4	0.4
Poland	1.1	1.0	0.9	0.9	0.8	0.9
Spain	1.5	1.2	1.2	1.5	1.2	3.6
Sweden	1.7	1.2	1.4	1.2	1.1	1.0
England and Wales	0.0	0.0	0.0	0.0	0.0	0.0
N Ireland	0.6	0.8	0.8	0.7	0.8	0.8
Russia	0.5	0.6	0.6	0.6	1.1	1.2
Morocco	0.0	0.0	0.0	0.0	0.0	0.0
Tunisia	0.1	0.1	0.1	0.1	0.8	0.3
TOTAL	19.4	19.4	19.4	16.6	19.1	18.7

These figures do not include eel catches made by weekend sports fishermen which, when they are all added together throughout Europe, North Africa, and Russia, could substantially increase the weight taken annually. In addition 600–700 tons of eels are caught yearly in Greece which are also not included. The main countries catching wild European eels in 1971 are clearly France, Denmark and Italy, with further limited quantities being taken in the Netherlands, Spain and Sweden. One of the factors determining the weight of wild eels captured is the number of eel fisherman available. There are indications in some countries, that the decrease in the number of eels taken is not due so much to a decrease in the number of eels available but to a decrease in the number of fishermen available. Eel fishing is a seasonal outdoor occupation which no longer attracts as many young men as it used to do. Many prefer the obvious security of factory life or of some other occupation, as opposed to following in their father's footsteps.

An important fact these figures reveal is that overall the weight of European eels caught has been relatively static, at about 19,500 tons annually, for a number of years. There are many people both conservationists and others who claim that the over-exploitation of European eels and elvers is leading to a decrease in the eel population. This does not appear to be so at the present time though, of course, it must be remembered that it takes a period of five to six years for an elver to reach a marketable size in the wild. Only after this length of time can the effects of any exploitation be observed. The distribution of the European eel is, however, so widespread that there are many many rivers which are not fished for eels at all, so that there is always a totally unexploited proportion of the population which can return, completely unmolested by man, to breed the next generation in the Sargasso Sea.

B. Japanese Eel

Table 30 – Weight of Japanese wild eels caught (1969–1974)

Country/Year	1969	1970	1971	1972	1973	1974
Taiwan	1.6	2.0	3.9	—	—	—
Japan	3.2	2.7	2.6	2.4	2.4	2.1
Korea	0.4	0.1	0.2	0.1	0.1	0.1
TOTAL	5.2	4.8	6.7	2.5	2.5	2.2

These figures do not include the tonnage of eels cultured in Japan which, if added in, would raise the total weight in 1969 to as high as 28,500 tons. This total was considerably in excess of the total weight of wild eels caught that year in Europe. The combined weight of both captured and cultured Japanese eels is, as a rule, slightly in excess of that of the total weight of European eels at about 20,000 tons. The figures given for Taiwan include a proportion of eels which have been cultured. No figures are given for the weight of Japanese eels caught on the Chinese mainland. There is, however, considerable speculation as to what quantities are involved and the influence these would have if they were to be suddenly introduced on to the eel market in Japan.

It has been reported, and it can be observed in many ways, that due to the combined effects of over exploitation and the increasing pollution of inland waters, the numbers of wild Japanese eels and elvers caught annually is decreasing. The rapid expansion of the Japanese eel culture industry in the 1950's apparently was not due solely to increased market demand but to a need to supplement decreasing numbers of wild eels.

C. American Eel

Table 31 – Weight of American eels caught (1969–1974)

Country/Year	1969	1970	1971	1972	1973	1974
Canada	1.1	1.1	1.2	1.1	0.7	0.7
American	0.9	1.0	1.1	0.9	1.1	1.1
TOTAL	2.0	2.1	2.3	2.0	1.8	1.8

The total quantity of wild American eels captured is negligible by comparison with the figures for the European eel and has been static for a number of years at, or around, 2,000 tons annually. There are some experts who believe this species of wild eel is still largely unexploited. This is perhaps due to both a lack of interest and hence demand from the home market, as well as only relatively few fisherman being trained in eel capture, because other types of occupation offer considerably better incomes. It is partly because of the lack of demand in North America that a number of attempts over the years have been made to export live American eels and elvers to Europe and the Far East. The weakness of their competitive position in comparison to the locally caught wild eels and the low profitability of such an operation, once air freight charges have been taken into consideration, limits the spread of American eel exports on a larger scale except for a few days at a time each year when, perhaps, market conditions are favourable. Some exports have been attempted by sea-shipment.

The eel capture industry in Canada is restricted mainly to Quebec, and to the St. Lawrence River area with only small quantities being caught in the other States. The United States of America provides a potential development area for eel culture from the viewpoint of climate suitability. However, the old problems of lack of home market and the need for a cultured product to compete economically with wild eels caught in Europe, or with an eel cultured and marketed in Japan, first have to be overcome before culture becomes a feasible proposition. The introduction of eel to the American market in a prepacked form backed by careful advertising may yet provide a profitable area for development.

D. New Zealand Eel

Table 32 – Weight of New Zealand eels caught (1969–1974)

Country/Year	1969	1970	1971	1972	1973	1974
Australia	0.2	0.1	0.2	0.2	0.0	0.0
New Zealand	0.4	0.9	1.5	2.1	1.3	0.8
TOTAL	0.6	1.0	1.7	2.3	1.3	0.8

The New Zealand eel is the only species of eel captured commercially in the Southern Hemisphere. New Zealand provides a classic example of how the sudden awareness of a potentially valuable resource is followed by exploitation, a rapid development of markets, and then over exploitation, and a decline in production. In 1967, only 100 tons of wild eel were caught; by 1971 this figure had grown to 1,500 tons and in the succeeding year 2,160 tons. This is a remarkable increase in production in such a short period of time.

The home consumption of eels is negligible in New Zealand, so processers and export agents are forced to search for potential, market outlets in Europe and the Far East. The relative isolation of New Zealand precludes the possibility, in most cases, of exporting live eels and places increased dependence on processed eels being produced and freighted at a low cost so as to remain competitive with their European and Far Eastern counterparts. The Australian output of wild eels is insignificant and is confined mainly to one or two processors outside Melbourne. Eels are still used in Australia as a bait for sharks.

VALUE OF WILD EELS CAUGHT ANNUALLY (US $)

The following figures given for the European, Japanese, American and New Zealand eels are in thousands of US dollars:

A. European Eel

Table 33 – Value of European eels caught (1969–1973) (US $)

Country/Year	1969	1970	1971	1972	1973
Denmark	5,123	5,776	7,334	7,904	9,779
France	1,523	3,991	6,754	3,861	7,011
Germany (Fed.)	912	875	1,301	1,151	1,452
S. Ireland	139	290	149	127	318
Italy	4,971	5,235	6,284	6,431	7,437
Netherlands	2,851	2,090	1,842	1,936	2,364
Norway	458	414	508	678	819
Spain	1,515	1,515	—	1,877	—
Sweden	2,906	2,547	3,269	3,085	3,296
England	22	17	23	30	76
N. Ireland	811	960	2,733	1,344	1,484
TOTAL	21,231	23,710	30,197	28,424	34,036

The total value of European eels caught in 1971, was in excess of $30m. A staggering figure which, possibly, few people are aware of. More than seven European countries had a turnover of $1m or more from eels. Although an eel is a snake-like creature, it has a very high commercial value. These figures do not include the value of catches made in the Communist countries, or in North Africa, so the actual final total value of catches made annually is, of course, even higher. The values given for each quoted country are the prices paid by wholesalers to eel fishermen and are not retail prices. A retailer may have a mark-up of between 15–30%, and a restaurant or hotel of 100% or more, so the final total value paid by consumers based on these figures for European eels is higher and excludes imported American, Japanese, and New Zealand eels. The total value of this market can also be seen to be increasing annually at a rapid rate – by nearly 50% in the three years between 1969 and 1971.

B. Japanese Eel

Table 34 – Value of Japanese wild eels caught (1969–1972)

Country/Year	1969	1970	1971	1972
Taiwan	2,937	—	—	—
Japan	—	—	—	—
Korea	86	103	247	323
TOTAL	3,023	103	247	323

The published data on the value of catches of wild and cultured Japanese eels is almost non-existent. This makes it impossible to have any worthwhile discussion on up-to-date figures. It is however, of interest to note that in 1968, when the last full figures are quoted, the combined market value of Japanese eels was nearly $50m in comparison with $21m for European eels. It can be stated with certainty that the Japanese eel market is worth as much as the European market and with caution that it is perhaps worth twice as much. The possible combined value of the two largest eel markets, namely Europe and Japan, was in 1971 an estimated $75m. Add to this a total value in the region of $10m for elvers imported by Japan and a total market value for eels in one form or another of circa. $85–90m is reached!

C. American Eel

Table 35 – Value of American eels caught (1969 – 1973) (US $)

Country/Year	1969	1970	1971	1972	1973
Canada	574	530	675	768	594
America	—	—	—	—	—
TOTAL	574	530	675	768	594

D. New Zealand Eel

Table 36 – Value of New Zealand eels caught (1969–1973)

Year	1969	1970	1971	1972	1973
New Zealand	60	130	259	438	366

The total value figures for American and New Zealand eels are incomplete and those given are included here only to fill out the picture as much as possible. It is a remarkable achievement and a credit to those involved that between 1966 and 1971, in the space of six years, the export value of New Zealand eels in New Zealand dollars, as opposed to landed value which is given above, increased from only $80,000 to over $1,000,000.

It can be a misleading exercise to divide total landed weights by total values in order to obtain a figure for the value to the catcher per landed ton of eels, as inaccuracies of declared figures are further compounded. However, the result does give an indication of the relative values paid to catchers for different species of eel without having to accept the final figures as being exact.

Table 37 – Average prices paid to catchers per ton of eels (U.S.$)

Species/date	1970	1971
European eel	1,440	1,920
Japanese eel	1,030	1,235
American eel	480	610
New Zealand eel	144	172

The figures clearly indicate European eel catchers receive the best prices for their eels and that, by comparison, American and New Zealand eel fishermen receive low returns.

LOCAL CURRENCY VALUE OF WILD EELS CAUGHT

The following monetary figures are expressed in terms of the local currency of each country quoted. They are included so as to give readers in different parts of the world a means of quickly understanding some of the figures in the currencies they normally work with.

A. European Eel

Table 38 – Value in local currencies of European eels (1969–1973) ('000)

Country/Year	1969	1970	1971	1972	1973
Denmark	38,435	43,322	51,194	55,117	58,507
France	846	2,205	3,455	1,975	3,086
Germany (Fed.)	3,339	3,201	4,194	3,671	3,771
S. Ireland	58	121	57	51	130
Italy	3,107	3,272	3,658	3,743	4,349
Netherlands	10,321	7,565	5,977	6,213	6,456
Norway	3,270	2,955	3,376	4,469	4,595
Sweden	15,036	13,176	15,735	14,650	14,342
England	9	7	9	12	31
N. Ireland	338	400	420	537	630

Once again these figures refer to the total of prices paid to eel catchers as opposed to the total retail or wholesale market values. The figures for Denmark are expressed as thousand Danish Kroner; France as ten thousand New Francs; Germany as thousand Deutschemarks; S. Ireland as thousand Irish pounds; Italy as million lire; Netherlands as thousand guilders; Norway as thousand Norwegian Kroner; Sweden as thousand Swedish kroner; England and N. Ireland as thousand pounds sterling. No further comment is necessary on these figures. Each reader can interpret and analyse them according to his own needs.

B. Japanese Eel

The total value of eel catches in local currencies for the Japanese eel recorded are incomplete, so they do not warrant inclusion.

C. American Eel

Table 39 – Value of Canadian eels ('000) 1969–1973

Country/Year	1969	1970	1971	1972	1973
Canada	621	573	730	761	594

No figures are quoted for the United States of America.

D. New Zealand Eel

Table 40 – Value of New Zealand eels ('000$) 1969–1973

Country/Year	1969	1970	1971	1972	1973
New Zealand	54	116	213	360	263

No figures are quoted for Australia and in any case catches are minimal.

AVERAGE PRICES PAID PER TON TO EEL CATCHERS

It can be a misleading exercise to divide total catch figures by prices paid in local currencies and US dollars so as to arrive at an average price paid to catchers for a ton of their eels. The average prices per ton paid to eel fishermen in 1971 includes both brown and silver eels with no differentiation being made between them. Silver eels, as it has already been noted, are considerably more valuable to the catchers than brown eels. All species of eel are grouped together as the figures for some countries are relatively incomplete.

Table 41 – Average price paid per ton to eel catchers

Country/price	U.S. Dollars	Local currency
Denmark	2,290	16,000 kroner
France	1,374	7,050 francs
Germany (Fed.)	2,600	8,390 marks
S. Ireland	1,490	570 pounds
Italy	1,900	1,108,000 lire
Netherlands	1,535	5,980 guilders
Norway	1,270	8,440 kroner
Sweden	2,515	12,100 kroner
N. Ireland	3,410	1,310 pounds
Canada	610	664 dollars
New Zealand	172	140 dollars

The average prices paid in US dollars provides an equal basis for comparing prices paid per ton to eel fishermen in different countries throughout the world. These figures indicate Northern Ireland eel fishermen receive the best prices for their brown and silver eels. Continuity of supply, the production of a guaranteed good quality eel which is ideal for processing and the speed and condition on delivery of live eels to the market backed by the successful co-ordinated organisation of eel fishermen, are all factors which enable high prices to be asked for and to be paid by processors in Europe. At the other end of the scale, eel catchers in Canada and New Zealand receive, by comparison, a low return for their eels.

EEL EXPORTS FROM PRINCIPAL EXPORTING COUNTRIES

The figures given in this section so far refer solely to weights of eels caught in their respective countries. There is, however, as in the elver trade, a large export market for eels. Countries with the highest level of production, as with many other products, are not necessarily the countries with the highest level of consumption. A complete coverage of eel exports throughout the world is not available from the *FAO Yearbook of Fishery Statistics*. For instance, the regular shipments of live eels from Northern Ireland to other parts of Europe, the export of frozen New Zealand eels to Europe, and the exports of live and frozen American eels to Europe, are not included. Only the principal exporting countries, as defined by FAO, are quoted. Eels are exported either fresh or chilled (still alive), frozen, smoked, or in other processed forms.

Fresh or Chilled Eel Exports/Imports

Table 42 – Quantity and value of Danish fresh eel exports (1969–1974)

Denmark	1969	1970	1971	1972	1973	1974
Quantity ('ooo tons)	4.1	4.0	3.4	3.7	3.6	3.5
Value (kroner)	50,122	54,913	58,606	68,295	70,264	77,629
US $ 'ooo	6,683	7,322	7,906	9,793	11,657	12,758
Destination						
Belgium & Luxemburg	0.7	0.5	0.4	0.3	0.3	0.4
Germany (Fed.)	2.1	2.0	1.9	2.1	2.1	2.0
Netherlands	1.0	1.1	1.0	1.1	1.0	1.0
Other	0.3	0.4	0.1	0.2	0.2	0.1

Table 43 – Quantity and value of French fresh eel exports (1969–1974)

France	1969	1970	1971	1972	1973	1974
Quantity ('000 tons)	2.4	2.7	3.3	3.2	3.0	3.0
Value (Francs)	1,506	1,909	3,001	3,624	4,934	4,724
US $'000	2,711	3,437	5,420	7,186	11,116	9,817
Destination:						
Italy	1.7	1.9	2.5	2.3	1.8	1.3
Belgium &						
Luxemburg	0.4	0.1	0.5	0.5	0.5	0.5
Spain	—	—	0.0	0.0	0.0	0.5
Other	0.3	0.7	0.3	0.4	0.7	0.7

Table 44 – Quantity and value of Dutch fresh eel exports (1969–1974)

Netherlands	1969	1970	1971	1972	1973	1974
Quantity ('000 tons)	1.1	1.1	1.0	0.9	0.9	1.2
Value (guilders)	7,464	9,448	9,238	9,039	8,708	11,427
US $'000	2,062	2,610	2,659	2,816	3,118	4,256
Destination:						
Germany (Fed.)	0.8	0.8	0.7	0.6	0.7	0.9
Other	0.3	0.3	0.3	0.3	0.3	0.3

These figures can, of course, be re-expressed in terms of the main European countries importing fresh or chilled eels.

Table 45 – Quantities ('000) imported and exported within Europe (1974)

Exporting Country	Importing Country					
	Belgium	Germany	Netherlands	Italy	Spain	TOTAL
Denmark	0.4	2.0	1.0	—	—	3.4
France	0.5	—	—	1.3	0.5	2.3
Netherlands	—	0.9	—	—	—	0.9
1974 TOTAL	0.9	2.9	1.0	1.3	0.5	6.6

Germany and Italy are both clearly the main countries in Europe importing fresh or chilled eels, whereas by comparison Denmark and France are the foremost exporters.

The export and import of eels is not confined solely to Europe. Japan imports sizeable quantities of live 'adult' eels from a wide range of countries, as can be seen from the following table referring to imports for 1973;

Table 46 – Japanese imports of eels for 1973 and 1974

Country of Origin	1973 Kg	1973 Yen ('000)	1974 Kg	1974 Yen ('000)
India	—	—	6,980	3,586
R. Korea	6,928	21,842	11,173	25,125
China	33,156	50,252	17,695	20,489
Taiwan	6,750,176	10,320,138	7,688,759	13,397,058
Hong Kong	2,598	4,157	225	360
Thailand	6,780	7,840	—	—
France	5,152	8,853	—	—
Singapore	407	889	740	817
Canada	1,000	908	—	—
USA	8,520	9,898	13,384	16,763
Malaya	2,088	3,269	—	—
Phillipines	349	539	100	140
New Zealand	75,880	48,752	452	1,620
Indonesia	41,348	42,629	—	—
TOTAL	6,934,382	10,519,966	7,739,508	13,465,958

These figures are taken from: Japan exports and imports; commodity by country, complied by Ministry of Finance. Published by Japan Tariff Association. Taiwan's dominance of this market can

Table 47 – Japan's live eel imports by month from Taiwan 1973 and 1974

Month	1973 (Kg)	1974 (Kg)
January	327,696	307,935
February	347,910	439,526
March	612, 115	547,473
April	609,820	712,617
May	605,700	695,008
June	653,290	839,730
July	1,013,298	1,136,652
August	789,333	779,913
September	480,824	619,312
October	414,131	444,525
November	364,814	445,464
December	531,200	720,604

be clearly seen. Table 47 gives the monthly breakdown of Japan's imports from Taiwan. The distribution of production and marketing throughout the year is interesting.

Frozen Eels

Table 48 – Quantity and value of Danish frozen eel exports (1969–1974)

Denmark	1969	1970	1971	1972	1973	1974
Quantity ('000 t)	0.2	0.1	0.1	0.2	0.2	0.2
Value (kroner)	2,648	2,369	2,132	4,081	5,246	4,187
$ ('000)	353	316	288	585	870	688

No destinations are given for the frozen product and Denmark is the only country quoted. Exports of frozen European eels are negligible. New Zealand is probably the leading exporter of frozen eels.

Smoked Eels

Table 49 – Quantity and value of Dutch smoked eels exported (1969–1974)

Netherlands	1969	1970	1971	1972	1973	1974
Quantity ('000 t)	0.4	0.4	0.3	0.4	0.3	0.3
Value (Guilders)	2,732	2,855	2,684	3,467	2,907	2,781
$ ('000)	755	789	772	1,080	1,041	1,036

Once again, no destination is given for the Dutch smoked eels, as relatively negligible quantities are involved. However, there is little doubt that West Germany is the main importer of this product.

The figures given in the preceding section for fresh, frozen, and smoked eel exports and imports indicate over 90 per cent of all eels exported in Europe are still alive, as opposed to being processed, an an estimated 45–55 per cent of all captured eels are exported within Europe

SOME NOTES ON DIFFERENT EUROPEAN WHOLESALE MARKETS

Introduction

These notes are not intended to be fully comprehensive but it is hoped they will provide a few useful guidelines for would-be exporters and importers of eels to and within Europe. Each European country should be discussed as a separate market for eels, rather than Europe as a whole being considered as one market. Each member country has its own market peculiarities as to what size, type, and form of eel is preferred; how an eel should be handled before marketing; the prices wholesalers are prepared to pay; and the form in which the wild eel is finally consumed. The notes cover the main countries importing eels, and are in part based on information provided by the Export Services Division of the Department of Trade and Industry, England. It will be appreciated there is a considerable variation in requirements between suppliers within the same country.

Italy

There is virtually no demand for smoked eels. The situation, however, for live eels is quite different. There is a variation in the demand between the summer and the winter months, when sales receive a large boost around Christmas time, as the eel forms one of the main items eaten during the festivities. Even though sizeable quantities of eels are caught in the Italian fresh water regions, there is still a strong demand for supplies to be supplemented. The largest supplier is France which supplies about three quarters of the weight of brown eels imported during the summer months and about half of the silver eels imported during the winter. The eel markets are centred mainly in Northern Italy in Milan, Turin, and Venice. The demand is mainly for live brown and silver eels grouped into four different size groups, namely 2–3, 3–5, 5–7 and 7–10 pieces per kilo.

France

The amount of smoked eel eaten in France is relatively small and the demand is easily supplied by home produced resources. All smoked eel processed locally is sold in chunky slices and tends to be rather fatty. France does not offer a potential outlet for either live or processed eels as it is one of the largest exporters in Europe. One or two importers occasionally express an interest in frozen silver and brown eels.

England

Only relatively few eels caught in England ever reach the market place. This is partly due to their distribution being so widespread and relatively thinly throughout the country. It is difficult for suppliers to catch or receive a sufficiently large quantity in any one place on a continuous basis to make it financially feasible to buy the specialised holding and transport equipment required to deliver to the London market. The market demand itself is small and falls into two categories namely jellied and smoked eels.

The demand for eels for jellying is met mainly by Northern Ireland, which supplies the right size live eels within 5–6 days of capture, on a regular basis. The trade generally prefers 3–5 pieces per kilo, though there is some variation between processors as a few prefer the smaller sized 5–7 pieces per kilo. On some occasions, when supplies have been available and the price low enough, New Zealand and American frozen and live eels have been used. There are some local processors who smoke eels on a very small scale to supply the luxury gourmet trade but in the main, smoked eels are imported from Holland and Germany. The eel market in England is therefore small and is satisfied principally by imports.

Belgium

A small scale wild eel catching industry is located along and near the North Sea coastline, together with a few supporting processors and wholesale market agents. Eel in one form or another is frequently offered on restaurant menus in the major cities such as Brussels and Antwerp. Fried eels, eels cooked with green herbs, or simply smoked eels, are all popular dishes. Belgium, of course, has a relatively small coastline and river system in which to catch eels, so considerable additional supplies of eel to satisfy home demand are imported from other European countries. The close proximity of Belgium to Holland, Germany, France and Denmark enable supplies of live eels to be delivered relatively easily.

Holland

If a product is offered at the right price there is always a demand for it. Holland produces a high tonnage of brown and silver eels from her own inland and coastal waters and is the base for many large scale eel dealers. The demand for eels, principally for smoking, is very high. A number of companies buy in live brown and silver eels both at home and from other continental countries, and maintain regular collections with lorries.

The best months for brown eels are between March and the end of July and, depending on the dealer, ideally the demand should fall into two size categories, either 8–10 eels per kilo, or 4–7 eels per kilo. Silver eels are taken in the late summer, autumn and early winter, and as a guideline eels weighing between 250 and 750 grams are sought (*ie* 2–3 eels per kilo).

There is not so much interest in frozen eels, as normally their quality is inferior to live eels thus making them less desirable for smoking.

Germany

This is a very big market for imported eels and is probably the most open eel market in Europe. Home supplies of wild and extensively cultured eels are not sufficient to meet demand. The main dealers are centred in the St. Pauli Fish Market in Hamburg and in Bonn. Importers buy in throughout the year. In the spring and summer they prefer live brown eels and in the autumn and winter, that is from October until March, live silver eels. The scale of operation is such that dealers collect the eels with their own special lorries fitted with water containers and redistribute them to different marketing outlets within Germany.

The ideal live eel should have a pointed head, be fat, healthy, and undamaged. Ninety per cent of the eels imported are smoked. The most popular eel weights are between 250–500 g and 500 g up to 1000 g. The smaller brown eels between 150–250 g each are not so much sought after and a lower price is paid for them. Only the highest quality brown eels are accepted. Prices paid, however, depend on supply and demand. Sometimes a cheaper price is paid for a 500–1000 g eel, than for one weighing 250–500 g, when the reverse should be true. This occurs, for instance, when catches of the large size eels are greater than the medium size and the market is over-supplied. Normally, about the same price is paid for both sized eels. Prices also depend on the size of a consignment, the weight of each eel, the type and quality of eel and the time of year in addition to supply and demand.

Germany imports live eels from all over Europe and Scandanavia. Varying quantities of eels are also imported from Canada, the United States of America, New Zealand and Japan, though the prices paid are generally much lower as the quality of these species of eel are not considered as good as that of the European eel. The Germans are prepared occasionally to buy in deep frozen eels which, preferably should not have been gutted beforehand, and are either single or block frozen. Smoked eels are also imported, mainly from Holland, preferably hot smoked so as to given them a very pale colour.

Denmark

The Danish are one of the main European people that catch eels. They export fresh and frozen eels principally to Germany and Holland. It is of interest though, that Denmark also imports substantial quantities of silver eels. In 1970, for instance. Denmark imported 1,415 tons of eels of which 50% came from Norway and Sweden. Additional supplies also come from the USA and Canada and dealers generally like to handle these alive. They are, of course, air freighted. Pointed head silver eels, as opposed to broad headed brown eels, are required. The main demand is for an eel weighing between 250 and 600 grams. If available they are taken in all the year round.

The larger dealers do not normally buy-in frozen eels because of their lower quality and difficulties involved in grading them before they are passed on to the smoker. Different smokers require different sized eels and this can lead to mistakes and disputes. Importers prefer the eels should be frozen alive, as this process draws the blood up under the skin and gives the colour preferred in Denmark.

In conclusion, the stages in the production and marketing of eels in Europe, are outlined in Fig 24.

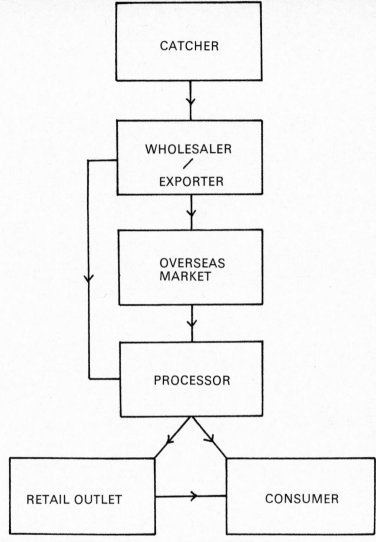

Fig 24   Stages in the production and marketing of eels in Europe

References

Much of the technical information included in this book has been drawn from the references given in the following list. I would like to express my sincere appreciation to the various authors and organisations involved in the compilation of this data and for the use of their material, without which, one of the main objectives of this book could not have been achieved, namely, to provide a comprehensive coverage of all published data relating to the main book section headings. Interested readers are strongly recommended to refer to these books or to the organisation responsible for their publication for further detailed information. The references have been subdivided, where possible, into eel culture, capture, processing and marketing, to aid reference.

CULTURE

Aker, E, Red disease of eel in the German Bight. *Arch. Fischereiwiss* 21 (3), 268–269 (1970).

Arai, S, Nose, T, Hashimoto, Y, A purified test diet for the eel, anguilla japonica; *Bulletin Freshwater Fish Research Laboratory* vol 21 No. 2 (1971).

Chen, T P, *Eel farming in Taiwan,* Joint Commission on Rural Reconstruction (1973).

Chen, T P, The fabulous eel industry, *Industry of Free China* (1971).

FAO/EIFAC, Report of the 1970 Workshop on fish feed technology and nutrition, production and feeding of eels in Japan. Notes taken during lectures of Messrs Nose and Suna, by Lerguet Muller-Feuga, A, First steps in eel production in Japan. *Rapp. Tech. Centl. Natl. Exploit. Oceans* (1972). French production.

Ghittino, P, *Diet and fish handling.*

Ghittino, P, et al, Residue determination of Metrifonat in fish and waters after therapeutic treatment with Masoten. *Riv. Ital. Piscre. Ittiopatol* 6 (4), 99–104 (1971).

Halver, J E, (1957) Nutrition of salmonoid fishes, 3 water soluble vitamin requirements of Chinook salmon, *Journal of Nutrition* 62, 225–243.

Hashimoto, Y, Arai, S, Nose, T, Amino acids essential for the growth of eels, anguilla anguilla and anguilla japonica. *Bull. Jap. Soc. Sci. Fish* 38 (7), 753–759.

Hashimoto, Y, Arai, S, Nose, T, Thiamine deficiency symptoms experimentally induced in the eel. *Bull. Jap. Soc. Sci. Fish* 36 (8); 791–797 (1970).

Hataya, M, *An introduction to eel culture.* Shizouka Fisheries Experimental Station (1972).

Hickling, C F, *Fish culture*, Faber & Faber, 1971.

Huet, M, *Textbook of fish culture; breeding and cultivation of fish.* Fishing News (Books) Ltd.

Ito, T, Iwai, T, *Prefectural University of Mei*, vol 3, No. 2 November 1959.

Koops, H, Cauliflower disease of eels. *Arch. Fischereiwiss* 29 (1), 1–52 (1971).

Koops, H, Feeding of eels (anguilla anguilla) in ponds. *FAO Fish Rep.* (44) vol 3, 359–364 (1967).

Meshe, C, Cellarius, D, Laboratory rearing of eels to sexual maturity. *Naturwissenchaften*, 59 (10), 471–472 (1972).

Nose, T, A preliminary report on some essential amino-acids for the growth of eel, anguilla japonica. *Bull. Freshwater Fish Res. Lab.* vol 19 No 1 (1969).

Nose, T, Arai, S, Optimum level of protein in purified diet for eel, anguilla japonica; *Bulletin of Freshwater Fisheries Laboratory* vol 22. No 2 (1972).

Onodera, K, Some data on eel-culture in Japan; *Indo Pacific Fisheries Council Occ. Paper* 62/6.

Sanders, M J, Australian studies Japanese fish culture techniques, *Australian Fisheries*, October 1971.

Shang Jung, C, Economic aspects of eel culture in Taiwan; Chinese-American Joint Commission on Rural Reconstruction, *Fisheries Series* No 14 (1973).

Usui, A, *Eel culture*, Fishing News (Books) Ltd. (1974).

Wakabayashi, H, Egusa, S, Characteristics of a pseudomonas sp. from an epizootic of pond cultured eels (anguilla japonica). *Bull. Jap. Soc. Sci. Fish* 38 (6) 577–587. (1972).

CAPTURE

Eales, T G, *The eel fisheries of Eastern Canada*; Fisheries Research Board of Canada (1968).

Horne, J, Birnie, K, Catching, handling and processing eels; Ministry of Technology; *Torry Research Station Advisory Note* 37 (1970).

McGrath, C J, (Ed); EIFAC Consultation on eel fishing gear and techniques; European Inland Fisheries Advisory Commision; *EIFAC Technical paper* No 14, Rome; October 10–17 1970.

MAFF: Basic principles of electric fishing; *Fisheries Notice;* Ministry of Agriculture, Fisheries and Food, October 1971.

Perrett, R, *Eels: how to catch them.* Barry and Jenkins, London.

PROCESSING

Horne, J, Birnie, K, Catching, handling and processing eels; Ministry of Technology; *Torry Research Station Advisory Note* 37 (1970).

Montague, P, *Larousse gastronomique*, Paul Hamlyn, London.

Pel, Van J, *Hot smoking of eel.* Institute for Fishery Products TNO, Holland.

MARKETING

Export Services Division, Department of Trade and Industry, London.

FAO catchings and landings 1973; *FAO Yearbook of Fishery Statistics.*

FAO fishery commodities 1973; *FAO Yearbook of Fishery Statistics.*

Fisheries statistics of Canada, Dominion Bureau of Statistics, Ottawa.

Japan exports and imports; Commodity by country; complied by Ministry of Finance, Japan Tariff Association.

Shearer, W M, The catching and marketing of eels. *Scottish Fisheries Bulletin*, No. 16.

The New Zealand eel and the European eel. New Zealand Trade Commissioner, London.

GENERAL

Bertin, J, *Eels: a biological study* (1956), Cleaver-Hume Press Ltd.

Commercial Fisheries Review, National Marine Fisheries Service (USA) March–April 1972.

Deelder, C L, Synopsis of biological data on the eel, anguilla anguilla (Linnaeus) 1958; *FAO fisheries synopsis No 80* (1970).

Eales, T G, Ms. A bibliography of the eels of the genus anguilla, Fish Res. Bd., Canada. *Tech. Rept. No 28.*

FAO Aquaculture Bulletins, Fisheries Division, FAO, Rome.

FAO General Fisheries Council for the Mediterranean, Rome 1972. *Report of the eleventh session*, Athens, Greece. 6–11 March 1972.

Fishing News International. Arthur J Heighway Publications Ltd. London.

Fish Farming International. Arthur J Heighway Publications Ltd. London.

Folsom, W B, Japan's eel fishery; *Marine fisheries review* vol 35 Nos 5–6. MFR Paper 984.

Jones, J L, Elvers forever. *The Countryman* vol 56 No 1 (1959).

Index

Aerators, in eel culture 48, 73, 77–83, 86–89
  in experiments 100–103
  in transport 38, 146
Aeromonas liquefaciens 54
Age of eel maturity 23, 125
Atlantic crossing 21–22
American eel (*Anguilla rostrata*) 27, 28, 176–177
  exports of 39, 41, 183, 185, 190
Ammonia 74
Anabaena 71
Anchor worm 55
Aquaria 100–101
Anguilla anguilla, see European eel
Anguilla australis, see New Zealand eel
Anguilla diffenbachi, see long-finned eel
Anguilla japonica, see Japanese eel
Anguilla marmorata, see mottled eel
Anguilla rostrata, see American eel
Area of farm 111
  of ponds 48–49, 51, 75–76, 79–80
  relative to production 115
Anguillicola grobiceps 56
Australian capture of eels 27, 177
  experiments 47, 69
  migration factors 29
Australian eel, see New Zealand eel
Austria 41
Authenticating live weight 37, 44

Bacteria 70 and see Prevention of disease
Bags 96
Bait 125, 130–133 passim

Baited eel box 131–132
Baltic 56
Barriers for catching eels 127, 139–144
Baskets for feeding 60, 79–83
  for transport 98, 99
Behaviour patterns see Life cycle
Belgium 183, 184, 188
Boiled eel 109, 166
Bones in feed 58–59
Bonn 189
Boxes for eels 147, 148, 152
  for elvers 38, 43
Brining 153, 154, 158
Bronchial kidney 53
Brown eel see European eel
Bruising 34–35, 37, 146
Bubble disease 55
Buoyed nets 34

Canadian, eel capture 27, 130–131
  exports 39, 41, 185, 190
  values 179–181
  weight 176–177
Canned eels 168
Cannibalism 65
Capture, of eels 123–144
  of elvers 25–27, 31–34
Carbonic acid 70
Cauliflower disease 57
Chemicals, for elver feed 65
  in disease control 52–56 and see Salinity
  in eel capture 125
China, eel capture 26, 175–176
  exports 39, 41, 185

Chlorococcus 71
Chlorella 71
Chondrococcus columnalis 53–54
Circulating filter method 51
Cleaning of eels 153–155
Clotting 128–129
Cold storage 153, 154, 157, 166
Combs, eel 130
Compound feed 60–65, 67, 68, 110
  and minerals in water 75
  mixer for 93, 97
  storage for 85
Condition factor 109
Conversion rates 50, 51, 57–61, 68–69
Copper sulphate 55
Costs, of boxes 38, 43, 147, 148, 152
  of elvers 39–41, 117, 118
  of equipment 115
  of feed 115, 117
  of heating 69
  of ponds 79
  of retarded growth 68
  of tanks 148
  of traps 135
  variable 117–119
Cotton cap (Water mould) 52, 54
Cuba 39, 41
Culture of eels, see Extensive and
  Intensive
Currents 21–22, 26–28
Cycles, of elvers 29

Denmark, eel capture 25, 129, 139
  market 190
  values 178, 181–184
  weight 174
Depth of water 77, 80, 100–103
Design, see Pond design
Dishes 169–170
Diptrex 55, 71
Disease 40, 51–56, and see
  Prevention
Disinfecting 52, 77
Drainage of farm 80, 81, 111–112
  of ponds 77–84, 89, 90, 95, 97
  in capture 108–109

Eel Farmers Federation 40, 42
Elbe 57
Electric fishing devices 47, 127, 135-137
Elver ponds 77–79, 88–92
Embryo 21
England, eel capture 134, 140
  elver capture 25, 29, 31–32
  exports 39, 41
  jellied eels in 165
  market in 188
  values 178, 181
  weight 174
Environment in intensive culture
  68–75
Equipment 85–99, and see Pond
  design
Escapes 47, 77, 90, 112
European eel (*Anguilla anguilla*) 21–25, 123–128, 166
  capture of 31–34, 128–144
  disease of 51–52, 53–56
  distribution of 24–25
  fatness and cost of 40, 165
  growth rate of 105–106
  life cycle of 21–24, 125–128
  migration of 28–29, 30–31, 124–128
  optimum temperature for 68
  values of 178, 180–181
  viability in intensive culture 110–121
  weight caught 174–175
Experimental feeding 101
  ponds 95, 99–103
  tanks 100–103
Exports 24, 39–41, 183–191
Extensive culture 45–46
Eyes of eels 125

Farm, see Area, Drainage, Layout
  Siene nets and Tanks
Fat content 125, 165
Fattening ponds 79–85, 90–96, 102–103
Feed 57–67, 115
  bowls for 99

cost of 117
equipment for 81–82, 85–89, 92
for elvers 62, 64–65, 89
methods for 60–61, 58
storage of 63–64, 85, 93
'Feeding' eel 23
Ferric oxide 74, 109
Fertilisation 21
Fin rot 54
Finance 116–120, and see Costs
Fingerling ponds 79, 102
Fishing gear 124, 125
Fixed installations 143–144
Flow rate in tanks 77–83
Flowing water circulation 49, 80
Formalin 56
France, eel capture 24–25, 34, 139, 143
   exports 39, 41, 46, 187, 188
    and see values
   extensive culture 46
   intensive culture 47–48, 121
   values 178, 181, 182, 184, 185
   weight 174
Freezing 144, 153, 154, 156, 157
   for jellied eel 166
Frozen exports 186
Furazolidone 52, 54
'Futo' farmer 106–107
Fyke nets 127, 138–139, 142, 151

Gelatine 166–168
German Bight 56
   eel capture 123, 139, 142
   exports 188
   imports 25, 41, 120
   intensive culture in 47
   markets 189–190
   migration pattern 29
   values 178, 181–184, 186
   weight 174
Gill erosion 53–54
Gill net 96, 108
Glass eels 29, 34, 40
Glazing 153, 154, 157
Grinder 85, 99, 115

Growth rates, and feed 57–58
   and heat 46, 47, 68, 69
   and oxygen 73
   and species 105–106
   economics of 115, 121
   experiments on 64, 115
   in nets 50
   in ponds 51
   in tunnels 50

Hamburg 189
Harvesting 81, 108–10
Heating 69, 77–78
Hibernation 59, 124, 126
Holding, eels 144–147
   elvers 35–37, 43, 56
Holding trays 32, 33, 38–39
Holland, eel capture 25, 131–132, 135, 139
   exports 186, 188
   jellied eels in 165, 188
   market in 189
   restocking 41, 120
   values 178, 181–184
   weight 174
Hong Kong 39, 41, 185
Hormones 106
Hot springs 50, 69
Hungary 41, 45

Ice 38–39, 150
Ichthyophthirius multifillis 54–55
Indonesia 185
Intensive culture 46–121
Italy, eel capture 45, 127, 140, 143
   exports 39, 41
   holding 147
   intensive culture 48
   markets 187
   values 178, 181, 182, 184
   weight 174

Japan, imports to 24, 34, 39–41, 185
   local consumption of eel 109
   yields in 106–107
   and see Intensive culture and
    Kabayaki

Japanese eel (*Anguilla japonica*),
  capture and distribution of **26**–28,
    31, 34,141
  disease of 51–57
  feeding of 57–65
  growth rates of 105–106
  optimum temperature for 68–69
  migration factors for 30–31
  values 40, 179, 181
  viability of culture of 111–121
  weight 175–176
Jellied eels 153, 154, 165–168

Kabayaki 109, 153, 168–169
Killing 153–155
Kilns 159–164, 168
Korea, eel capture 26
  exports 39, 41, 185
  values 41, 179, 185
  weight 39, 175–176

Laboratory equipment 98, 99
Ladders in capture 33
Larousse Gastronomique 153, 169
Larvae 21–23
Layout of farm 84
Lernaea cyprinacea 55
Life cycle in eels 21–24, 125–128
Light, in capture 125–128, 143
  in feeding 35, 65
  in migration 30
  in pond design 78, 81, 97
Lime, in disinfection 52
  in pH control 72
  in phytoplankton control 71
  storage for 98
Long-finned eel (*Anguilla diffenbachi*)
  27
Long lines 125, 128, 130–131, 151
Losses of eels 108, 113–120
  of elvers 37, 39, 105
  and see Diseases
Lukang TFRI 46, 62–63
Luxemburg 183, 184

Mackerel 30, 66–67, 85

Madagascar 141
Malachite green 52
Malaya 39, 185
Management, of elvers 37
  of farm 102–110
  personnel 115–116
Masoten 55
Maturity of eels 23, 125
Marketing, of eels 144, 152, 153, 167,
    171–191
  of elvers 39–41
Markets, wholesale 115, 187–191
Mediteranean 56
Metamorphoses 22, 23
Methylene blue 52, 55
Microseisms 127
Migration factors, and eels 124–128
  and elvers 21–32
Mincing 58, 99
Minerals in compound feeds 62
  in water 74–75
Moon 124, 126
Mottled eel (*Anguilla marmorata*) 27
Morrocco 39, 174
Mud, in ponds 47, 79, 98

Nematodes 56
Net preserve cultivation 49–50
Nets, see Buoyed, Drag, Fyke, Scoop,
    Seine, Stow and Weir Nets
New Zealand 47 and see New
    Zealand eel
New Zealand eel (*Anguilla australis*)
    27–28, 30–31
  capture **34**, 139
  exports 39, 41, 182, 185, 186, 188,
    190
  fat content of 165
  fins 166
  values 180, 182
  weight 177
Nicrocystis 71
Nitrogen 55, 74–75
Northern Ireland, eel capture 25, 27,
    29, 33, 140
  extensive culture 45, 120, 123

supplies from 188
transport 148
values 178, 181–183, 185
weight 174
Norway 25, 174, 178, 181, 182
Nursery ponds 75–76
Nylon brush 33–34

Oscillatoria 71
Oxygen, and elvers 33, 35, 37, 38, 43–44
   and feeding 60
   and holding eels 146
   from phytoplankton 48, 69–71
   in too large supply 55
   in transport 38, 110, 148–150
   in water flow 49, 56, 72–74
   tests for 108

Paddles, see Aerators and Feeding
Palacolobacterum anguillimortiferum 54
Parasites see Diseases
Pectoral fin development 125
Pediastrum 71
pH 72, 114
   control by phytoplankton 70–71
   in Cotton cap control 52
Phillipines 39, 41, 185
Phosphate 74–75
Phytoplankton 48
   and chemicals 74–75
   management of 69–72, 81, 108, 111–113
Pigmentation 29, 125
Plistophora anguillarum 55
Poland 174
Pollution 27, 74, 113–114, 149
Pond design and equipment 75–103
Potassium 74–75
Potential markets 120–121
Power station 69
Predators 114, 115
Pre-shipment, starvation for 37, 64, 96, 109–110, 145
Prevention of disease 51–56 passim, 59, 79, 108, 115, 146

Prices, see Costs and Values
Processing 153–171
Protein 62–64
Protozoa 54–55
Pseudomonas punctata 56
Pumps 36, 38, 43, 51 and see Pond design and equipment

Quantity of feed 57–61, 108

Racks 46
Rate of travel 21–24, 128
Raw fish feed 50, 58–59, 63, 64, 66, 67
   equipment for 85, 99, 115
   pre-shipment starvation 110
Reception tank 35, 36
Red disease 56
Respiration 37–39, 144, 150
Restocking, in Europe, eels 120
   elvers 25, 31, 33, 41, 45
   in New Zealand 34
Revenue 119–120, 147, 174
Roofs 35, 87–92
Russia 174

Salinity of water 38, 53, 55–57, 146
Saproleania parasitica 52
Scendesmus 71
Scoop nets 31–32, 34, 43, 96, 108
Scotland 25
Seasons of runs 28–29, 124–128, 139–144
Security 86, 92, 94, 98–99, 115
Seine nets, for wild eels 34, 137–138
   in farm use 93, 96, 97, 108
Selection 104, 105, 108–110, 146
Sense organs 125
Shelter 125, 141
Shizouka 26, 49, 64, 76, 109
Short-finned eel, see New Zealand eel
Shovels 98, 99
Silkworm pupae feed 57–58, 66, 93
Silver eel, see European eel
Singapore 185
Slat widths 94, 97–98

Smoking 153, 154, 158–165
  and exports 186
  and markets 187–190
  and other uses 168, 171
Southern Ireland, eel capture 25, 33–
    34, 127
  exports from 46
  values 178, 181, 182
  weight 174
Spain 41, 48, 174, 178
Spawning conditions 21
  grounds 21, 26–28
Spears 129, 141
Still water cultivation 48, 80
Stocking density 46–47, 51, 103–104,
    118
  and oxygen 49, 58, 73
  pre-shipment 110
Storage 98, 99
Stow nets 141–142
Substrata 112
Sulpha drugs 54
Sulphamonomethoxine 65
Sulphur 74, 109
Sunshine see Phytoplankton
Sweden, eel capture 25
  values 178, 181, 182
  weight 174

Taiwan, eel capture 26, 34, 40
  exports 39, 41, 185, 186
  Fisheries Research Institute 46, 62–
    63
  values 179
  weight 175–176 and see
    Intensive culture passim
Tanks, holding 35–37
  observation 127
  on farms 77–78, 87–95
  pre-shipment 110, 146
  transporting 38, 147–150
Taoyuan 46
Temperature see Water
Thailand 185
Thiazine 52

Thunderstorms 125, 128
Tide 30–32, 40
Training elvers 64–65
Transport, of eels 147–150, 152, 189
  of elvers 37–39, 43
Traps 127, 128, 132–135, 139
Tunisia 174
Tunnel cultivation 50
Turnover 107

Urethan solution 101

Values of eels caught 178–185
  of elvers 40–41
Variation in elver size 29
Vibrio anguillarum 56
Vitamin oil 60–62, 64, 97
Vump 34–36, 149

Wages in Japan 117
Waikato R. 27
Water, availability 49, 112–113
  flow 31–37, and see Pond design
  temperature 46, 47, 49, 68–69
    and see Pond design and
    equipment
Waste in ponds 74, 101, 112, 114
  and see bones
Water mould, see Cotton cap
Weight, loss of 23, 64, 68, 110
  in growth stages 28, 29, 101, **120,
    123, 125**
  in gutting 155
  in smoking 162
Weight, of eels captured 174
  of elvers imported 39
Weir nets 142
Weirs 140–142
White spot 54–55
Whites 37
Windermere 23, 127
Wind 31, 112–113, 127
Worms 65 and see Anchor and
    Nematodes

Yana 141
Yellow eel, see European eel
Yields 106, 189

Zoo-plankton 54–55, 70–71

List of other books published by Fishing News Books Limited

Free catalogue available on request

A living from lobsters
Better angling with simple science
British freshwater fishes
Coastal aquaculture in the Indo-Pacific region
Commercial fishing methods
Control of fish quality
Culture of bivalve molluscs
Eel culture
Escape to sea
European inland water fish: a multilingual catalogue
FAO catalogue of fishing gear designs
FAO catalogue of small scale fishing gear
FAO investigates ferro-cement fishing craft
Farming the edge of the sea
Fish and shellfish farming in coastal waters
Fish catching methods of the world
Fish farming international 1, 2 and 3
Fish inspection and qualiy control
Fisheries oceanography
Fishery products
Fishing boats of the world 1
Fishing boats of the world 2
Fishing boats of the world 3
Fishing ports and markets
Fishing with electricity
Freezing and irradiation of fish

Handbook of trout and salmon diseases
Handy medical guide for seafarers
How to make and set nets
Inshore craft of Britain in the days of sail and oar
Inshore fishing: its skills, risks, rewards
International regulation of marine fisheries: a study of regional
    fisheries organizations
Introduction to trawling
Japan's world success in fishing
Marine pollution and sea life
Mechanization of small fishing craft
Mending of fishing nets
Modern deep sea trawling gear
Modern fishing gear of the world 1
Modern fishing gear of the world 2
Modern fishing gear of the world 3
Modern inshore fishing gear
More Scottish fishing craft and their work
Multilingual dictionary of fish and fish products
Netting materials for fishing gear
Power transmission and automation for ships and submersibles
Refrigeration on fishing vessels
Seafood fishing for amateur and professional
Ships' gear 66
Sonar in fisheries: a forward look
Stability and trim of fishing vessels
Testing the freshness of frozen fish
Textbook of fish culture; breeding and cultivation of fish
The fertile sea
The fish resources of the ocean
The fishing cadet's handbook
The lemon sole
The marketing of shellfish
The seine net: its origin, evolution and use
The stern trawler
The stocks of whales
Trawlermen's handbook
Tuna: distribution and migration
Underwater observation using sonar